Number Tools

BRITANNICA
Mathematics
in
Context

Number

TEACHER'S GUIDE

HOLT, RINEHART AND WINSTON

Mathematics in Context is a comprehensive curriculum for the middle grades. It was developed in 1991 through 1997 in collaboration with the Wisconsin Center for Education Research, School of Education, University of Wisconsin-Madison and the Freudenthal Institute at the University of Utrecht, The Netherlands, with the support of the National Science Foundation Grant No. 9054928.

The revision of the curriculum was carried out in 2003 through 2005, with the support of the National Science Foundation Grant No. ESI 0137414.

National Science Foundation

Opinions expressed are those of the authors
and not necessarily those of the Foundation.

van Galen, F.; van den heuvel-Panhuizen, M.; Abels, M.; Dekker, T.; Querelle, N.; Pligge, M. A.; and Meyer, M. R. (2006). *Number tools.* In Wisconsin Center for Education Research & Freudenthal Institute (Eds.), *Mathematics in context.* Chicago: Encyclopædia Britannica, Inc.

ISBN 0-03-040428-2

2 3 4 5 6   073   09 08 07 06

The *Mathematics in Context* Development Team

Development 1991–1997

The initial version of *Number Tools* was developed by Frans van Galen and Marja van den Heuvel-Panhuizen. It was adapted for use in American Schools by Margaret A. Pligge.

Wisconsin Center for Education Research Staff

Thomas A. Romberg
Director

Joan Daniels Pedro
Assistant to the Director

Gail Burrill
Coordinator

Margaret R. Meyer
Coordinator

Freudenthal Institute Staff

Jan de Lange
Director

Els Feijs
Coordinator

Martin van Reeuwijk
Coordinator

Project Staff

Jonathan Brendefur
Laura Brinker
James Browne
Jack Burrill
Rose Byrd
Peter Christiansen
Barbara Clarke
Doug Clarke
Beth R. Cole
Fae Dremock
Mary Ann Fix

Sherian Foster
James A, Middleton
Jasmina Milinkovic
Margaret A. Pligge
Mary C. Shafer
Julia A. Shew
Aaron N. Simon
Marvin Smith
Stephanie Z. Smith
Mary S. Spence

Mieke Abels
Nina Boswinkel
Frans van Galen
Koeno Gravemeijer
Marja van den Heuvel-Panhuizen
Jan Auke de Jong
Vincent Jonker
Ronald Keijzer
Martin Kindt

Jansie Niehaus
Nanda Querelle
Anton Roodhardt
Leen Streefland
Adri Treffers
Monica Wijers
Astrid de Wild

Revision 2003–2005

The revised version of *Number Tools* was developed by Mieke Abels, Truus Dekker, and Nanda Querelle and was adapted for use in American Schools by Margaret A. Pligge and Margaret R. Meyer.

Wisconsin Center for Education Research Staff

Thomas A. Romberg
Director

David C. Webb
Coordinator

Gail Burrill
Editorial Coordinator

Margaret A. Pligge
Editorial Coordinator

Freudenthal Institute Staff

Jan de Lange
Director

Truus Dekker
Coordinator

Mieke Abels
Content Coordinator

Monica Wijers
Content Coordinator

Project Staff

Sarah Ailts
Beth R. Cole
Erin Hazlett
Teri Hedges
Karen Hoiberg
Carrie Johnson
Jean Krusi
Elaine McGrath

Margaret R. Meyer
Anne Park
Bryna Rappaport
Kathleen A. Steele
Ana C. Stephens
Candace Ulmer
Jill Vettrus

Arthur Bakker
Peter Boon
Els Feijs
Dédé de Haan
Martin Kindt

Nathalie Kuijpers
Huub Nilwik
Sonia Palha
Nanda Querelle
Martin van Reeuwijk

Cover photo credits: (left) © Getty Images; (middle, right) © Corbis

Illustrations
2, 3, 5, 45, 46 Christine McCabe/© Encyclopædia Britannica, Inc.

Contents

Contents

Introduction

The *Number Tools* are extra practice and extension problems to develop students' conceptual understanding, procedural fluency, and strategic competence with number and measurement. Some of the problems go beyond typical content goals for middle grades mathematics. These problems are designed as challenge problems and extension activities for students who are motivated to explore advanced topics in number.

Two resources are offered for *Number Tools*: a Teacher's Guide with blackline masters that can be photocopied for student use and a consumable Student Workbook. In the Teacher's Guide resource, blackline masters appear on the left-hand pages. Opposite them, on the right-hand pages, are solutions for teacher use. Some practice activities run longer than one page; in those instances, they are continued on the following left-hand page.

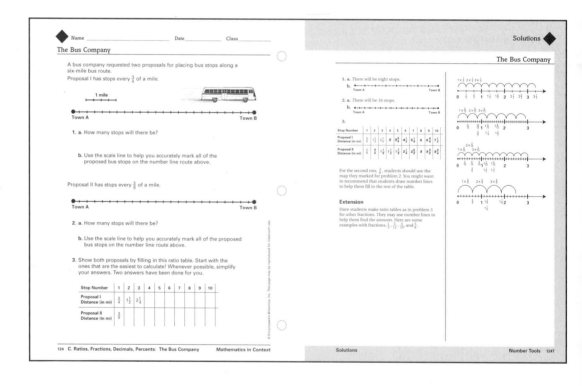

This resource follows the learning lines from the *Mathematics in Context* grade 6 through 8 number and measurement units, but can be used independently from this curriculum. There is no implied order to the sections or the pages within each section as long as the topic addressed has been adequately introduced. Activities can be completed in class or assigned as homework whenever you feel that your class needs extra practice or review.

Overview

The activities in Number Tools reinforce students' understanding of ratios, fractions, decimals, and percents, and the connections among these representations. While the number sense theme is embedded in all the Number units, this theme is emphasized in *Number Tools*. It is more important for students to understand computation and use their own accurate computation strategies than it is for them to use formal algorithms that they do not understand.

Throughout the Number and Measurement strands, models are important problem-solving tools because they develop students' understanding of fractions, decimals, percents, and ratios and help them to make connections. In Number Tools, extra practice for working with these tools is provided, for example, the ratio table, the number line, the empty number line, the double number line, and a fraction bar and percent bar. An example of the use of a ratio table:

Minutes	10	20	80	5	15	.....		
Miles	$\frac{1}{2}$	1	4	$\frac{1}{4}$	$\frac{3}{4}$	$4\frac{3}{4}$		

Many activities relate to the Algebra strand in the sense that in this workbook students practice using numbers, whereas in the *Algebra Tools* students prove the rules they found using expressions. Here is a typical example to show this relationship:

This rectangle is divided into four parts.

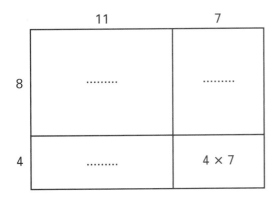

- Fill in the missing numbers on each part.

- Finish this number sentence showing the computation:

   $(8 + 4) \times (11 + 7) = 8 \times 11 + 8 \times 7 + ... \times .... + ... \times ....$

- Consider the number sentence showing this computation:
   $(10 + 2) \times (10 + 8)$.

   How do you know, without computing, the answer is the same as in the previous question?

Introduction

In *Algebra Tools,* we build on this concept when using the same area model with expressions:

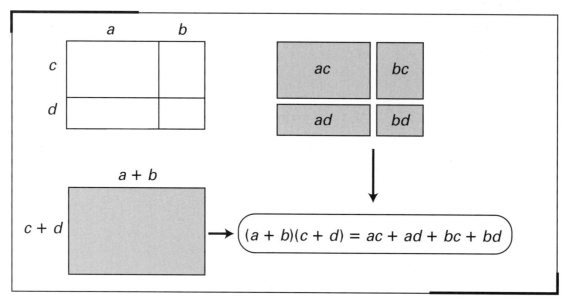

The diagram shows an algebra rule:

the product of the sums $a + b$ and $c + d$ is equal to the sum of the products ac, ad, bc, and bd.

- Use this rule to calculate the following products. Make an area model yourself.

$43 \times 57 = (40 + 3) \times (50 + 7) = $ .... = ...

$47 \times 53 = $ .... = ... = ...

In general, it is a good idea to let students produce their own examples or to design a similar exercise as shown in the workbook. This principle of asking students to make their own problems is usually very fruitful because of the reflection involved and the need to understand underlying principles at play in the structure of the series of problems.

On the *Mathematics in Context* website, mic.hrw.com, applets for additional practice also can be found.

Mathematics Content Addressed in *Number Tools*

As students work with the *Number Tools*, they will practice:

- developing number sense;
  - Students use different expressions and operating signs for computations.
  - Students use a variety of strategies to make computations easier to do mentally.
  - Students decide when to use a calculator and when to make a mental calculation.
  - Students make estimations and decide when an estimated answer is sufficient.
  - Students use number sense to solve a variety of unfamiliar problems.
  - Students round off large numbers and prices.
- understanding powers and the number system;
  - Students use large numbers, their names and scientific notation using powers of ten.
  - Students practice operations with powers.
- using arrow language to make calculations easier;
  - Students use arrow strings to understand the order of operations.
  - Students use arrow strings to understand inverse operations.
- working flexibly with fractions, decimals, and percents and their relationship;
  - Students use different representations like bars and number lines
  - Students use the place of the decimal point to understand decimals
- using ratios;
  - Students use compound units like miles per hour, miles per gallon, number of cell phones per 1,000 people, price per kilogram, and so on.
- working with two measurement systems; and
  - Students use the metric system.
  - Students use the customary system.
- using a variety of models as problem solving tools.
  - Students use ratio tables, number lines as well as empty number lines, double number lines and percent bars to solve problems.

What's in a Number?

How would you describe the number 52? You might say:

52 is 2 × 26;

52 is 4 × 13;

52 is two quarters and two pennies; or

52 is the age of Anton's father.

1. Write down several other ways to describe the number 52.

2. Write down several ways to describe the number 12.

3. Write down several ways to describe the number 24.

4. Choose your favorite number, and describe it in several ways.

What's in a Number?

1. Some sample descriptions for the number 52:
   - an even number;
   - the number of weeks in a year;
   - the name of a rock group (the B-52's);
   - the number of playing cards in a deck.

2. Some sample descriptions for the number 12:
   - the same age as Jim, my classmate;
   - 2×6;
   - half my brothers age;
   - $48 \div 4$;
   - one dime and two pennies.

3. Some sample descriptions for the number 24:
   - an even number;
   - the name of a popular television show, based on 24 hours in a day;
   - $2 \times 2 \times 2 \times 3$;
   - 4×6;
   - a number divisible by 2, 3, 4, 6, 8, 12, and 24;
   - $\frac{1}{2} \times 48$.

4. Answers will depend on the numbers students choose.

   Note: Encourage students to be creative and discuss answers in class.

Extension

Play *20 Questions* with numbers. Think of a number and then have the students take turns asking questions that can be answered with a *yes* or a *no*. The students' objective is to discover your number. A question such as, *Is the number 12* is only allowed as the final question. Students may ask:

- Is it an even number?
- Is it greater than 10?
- Is it a multiple of 5?
- Is it a multiple of 3?
- Could it be somebody's age?
- Could it be a year?
- Is it the year of the Bolshevik Revolution in Russia?
- Is it 1917?

The Plus or Minus Operations Game

The Plus or Minus Operations Game

Number of players: Two or more

Rules:

- Each player must reach a target number by adding and/or subtracting a list of numbers.
- Players must use all of the numbers at least once.
- Players may use some numbers more than once.
- The winner is the player who reaches the target number using the fewest operations.

Example:

| 3 | 5 | 9 | 10 | **25** |

Judy used 5 operations: $3 + 5 + 9 + 10 + 3 - 5 = 25$.

Maritza used 6 operations: $3 + 5 + 9 + 10 + 10 - 9 - 3 = 25$.

Judy won, because she used only five operations while Maritza used six.

Play the game with the following numbers:

1. | 3 | 6 | 7 | 8 | **39** | **2.** | 3 | 5 | 4 | 9 | **32** |

3. | 17 | 20 | 8 | 10 | **74** | **4.** | 5 | 11 | 16 | 4 | **53** |

5. | 15 | 8 | 14 | 20 | **91** | **6.** | 13 | 9 | 15 | 12 | **68** |

7. Make up two of your own problems.

The Plus or Minus Operations Game

1.–6.

The number of operations used for each problem will vary. Some sample number sentences.

1. $3 + 6 + 7 + 8 + 7 + 8 = 39$ 5 operations

     $3 + 3 + 6 + 6 + 6 + 7 + 8 = 39$ 6 operations

2. $3 + 5 + 4 + 9 + 5 + 9 - 3 = 32$ 6 operations

     $3 + 3 + 3 + 9 + 4 + 5 + 5 = 32$ 6 operations

3. $17 + 20 + 8 + 10 + 8 + 10$
    $+ 8 + 10 - 17 = 74$ 8 operations

     $17 + 20 + 8 + 10 + 10$
     $+ 17 - 8 = 74$ 6 operations

4. $16 + 16 + 16 + 5 + 11 + 4$
    $- 11 - 4 = 53$ 7 operations

     $5 + 11 + 16 + 4 + 4 + 4$
     $+ 4 + 5 = 53$ 7 operations

5. $15 + 8 + 14 + 20 + 14$
    $+ 20 = 91$ 5 operations

     $15 + 14 + 20 + 15 + 15$
     $+ 20 - 8 = 91$ 6 operations

6. $13 + 9 + 15 + 12 + 12$
    $+ 13 + 9 - 15 = 68$ 7 operations

     $13 + 15 + 12 + 12 + 13$
     $+ 12 - 9 = 68$ 6 operations

7. Use student generated problems to play the game with the entire class.

Note: The order in which students write their answers does not matter; the number of operations used is more important. Also, make sure that every number is used at least once.

Some of these problems are more difficult than they look. Here are some probing questions you can use to encourage students.

- What operations can you use to get close to the target number? What adjustments can you make to come close to the target number? Keep making adjustments until you reach the target number.

- Can you use fewer operations?

Blots (page 1)

Alphonse and Sarah decided to do their homework together. They soon discovered their worksheet had gotten wet, and the ink had blotted some of the numbers. One problem on the worksheet looked like this:

$$6 \times 4\blacksquare =$$

1. How many different answers could this problem have?

At first, they thought they could not do the problem. Alphonse decided to be creative and wrote this answer, "The product is more than 240 and less than 294." Sarah agreed but thought that the answer could also include the numbers 240 and 294.

2. Who is correct? Explain why you agree with Sarah or Alphonse.

Ms. Marne complimented Alphonse and Sarah for being diligent in completing their work! The class discussion was thought provoking, so she decided to make up some more blot-problems.

3. Find the range of possible answers to these blot problems. For each problem, the blot covers only one digit.

	The answer ranges from…		The answer ranges from…
a. $8 \times 3\blacksquare =$ ____ to ____		f. $6 \times 5\blacksquare =$ ____ to ____	
b. $5 \times 7\blacksquare =$ ____ to ____		g. $5 \times 2\blacksquare =$ ____ to ____	
c. $7 \times 8\blacksquare =$ ____ to ____		h. $3 \times 3\blacksquare =$ ____ to ____	
d. $4 \times 2\blacksquare =$ ____ to ____		i. $6 \times 4\blacksquare =$ ____ to ____	
e. $3 \times 9\blacksquare =$ ____ to ____		j. $9 \times 3\blacksquare =$ ____ to ____	

Mathematics in Context

1. There are 10 different answers to this problem. The one's digit of blotted number can be from 0 to 9; so the possible problem ranges from 6 × 40 through 6 × 49. Three sample answers:

   6 × 41 = 246

   6 × 45 = 270

   6 × 48 = 288

2. Sarah is correct. Explanations will vary. Sample explanation:

   The last digit, which is blotted, could be zero or nine.

   If the last digit is zero, the answer is 6 × 40 = 240.

   If the last digit is nine, the answer is 6 × 49 = 294.

Note: Students may have trouble understanding where the numbers 240 and 294 came from. Ask, *What are the smallest and largest digits that could have been where the blot is?* (The smallest digit is zero, so the smallest possible answer is 6 × 40 = 240. The largest digit is nine, so the largest possible answer is 6 × 49 = 294.)

3. The answer ranges from:

   a. 240 to 312

   b. 350 to 395

   c. 560 to 623

   d. 80 to 116

   e. 270 to 297

   f. 300 to 354

   g. 100 to 145

   h. 90 to 117

   i. 240 to 294

   j. 270 to 351

Blots (page 2)

4. Find the range of possible answers to these blot-problems.
In each problem, the second number is a three-digit number.

	The answer ranges from...
a. 3×3⬛⬛ =	_____ to _____
b. 6×4⬛2 =	_____ to _____
c. 9×2⬛0 =	_____ to _____
d. 4×6⬛9 =	_____ to _____
e. 8×53⬛ =	_____ to _____
f. 2×25⬛ =	_____ to _____
g. 3×62⬛ =	_____ to _____
h. 6×54⬛ =	_____ to _____
i. $3 \times$⬛70 =	_____ to _____
j. 7×24⬛ =	_____ to _____

5. Which problems were easiest? Which were more
challenging?

Mathematics in Context

4. The answers range from

   a. 900 to 1,197

   b. 2,412 to 2,952

   c. 1,800 to 2,610

   d. 2,436 to 2,796

   e. 4,240 to 4,312

   f. 500 to 518

   g. 1,860 to 1,887

   h. 3,240 to 3,294

   i. 510 to 2,910

   j. 1,680 to 1,743

5. Opinions about the most and least challenging problems will vary. Here is one sample opinion.

Problem **i** was most challenging because I had to change my routine, a three-digit number cannot begin with a leading zero. Problem **c** is probably the easiest because it ends in a zero, making the product easier to calculate.

Raffle Tickets (page 1)

This year, Johnson School is celebrating its 80th anniversary by having a Jubilee with live music and a raffle. Local businesses have donated items for the raffle. During the celebration, students will sell raffle tickets to raise money for the school library.

Here is a packet of raffle tickets that Sandra plans to sell. Notice that each raffle ticket has a number and the tickets are in numerical order.

1. List a few of Sandra's ticket numbers.

Gill's packet of raffle tickets number from 0401 to 0500.

2. List a few of Gill's ticket numbers.

Mary's packet of raffle tickets number from 1201 to 1300.

3. List a few of Mary's ticket numbers.

4. Do Sandra, Gill, and Mary have the same number of tickets to sell? Explain.

Here is Chantrea's packet of raffle tickets after selling some tickets. The number of the ticket on the top of her packet is No. 3414.

5. What ticket numbers were in Chantrea's original packet? How do you know?

6. How many tickets has Chantrea sold so far?

1. Sandra's ticket numbers must range from 0101 to 0200. Sample answer:

   A few of Sandra's ticket numbers are 0111, 0200, or 0197.

2. Gill's ticket numbers must range from 0401 to 0500. Sample answer:

   A few of Gill's ticket numbers are 0401, 0444, or 0494.

3. Mary's ticket numbers must range from 1201 to 1300. Sample answer:

   A few of Mary's ticket numbers are 1222, 1299, 1300.

4. Yes, they have the same number of tickets to sell. Sample explanation:

   Even though the numbers *on* the tickets are different, the number *of* the tickets is the same. From 401 up to 500 is 100 tickets, and from 201 up to 300 is also 100 tickets; if I isolate the last two digits, it is like counting 1, 2, 3, … 98, 99, up to 100.

5. Chantrea's packet contained ticket numbers 3401 to 3500. Sample explanation:

   Because Chantrea has the ticket number 3414, her packet must have contained all numbers in the 3400s, starting with 3401. Since all students had 100 tickets, her pack must end with number 3500.

6. Chantrea has sold 13 tickets, ticket numbers 3401 to 3413.

   Note: You might want to ask, *How can you represent this calculation?*

   A straight subtraction, $3413 - 3401$ does not lead to a correct answer because 3401 needs to be counted. Students must either adjust difference to be $3413 - 3400$ or adjust their calculation by adding 1 on at the end; $3413 - 3401 + 1$.

Raffle Tickets (page 2)

Mr. Han is one of the parents attending the party at the Jubilee. He buys several tickets.

7. If his first ticket is No.1235 and his last ticket is No. 1247, how many tickets did Mr. Han buy?

8. From which student did Mr. Han buy his tickets? How do you know?

At the end of the celebration, students must turn in their leftover tickets along with the money they collected. Here is the packet Sandra turned in. She sold up to ticket No. 0178.

9. How many tickets did Sandra turn in?

Here are Gill and Mary's leftover tickets.

Gill's Tickets   **Mary's Tickets**

10. How many tickets did each person turn in?

7. Mr. Han bought 13 tickets, numbered from 1235 to 1247.

8. Mr. Han bought his tickets from Mary; she had tickets 1201 to 1300.

9. 23 tickets, numbered from 1078 to 1100.

10. Gill: 18 tickets; numbered from 0483 to 0500.

 Mary: 44 tickets, numbered from 1257 to 1300.

Notes:

7. Students may be tempted to subtract 1235 from 1247, but this does not account for the total number of tickets. You might focus their attention on tickets numbered from 1235 to 1240; 1235, 1236, 1237, 1238, 1239, 1240. There are six tickets, but the difference, 1240 − 1235, accounts for only 5 tickets. Students need to adjust the calculation 1240 − 1234 to count ticket number 1235 or always add one on at the end 1240 − 1235 + 1. Both calculations will account for all the tickets.

9.–10.

 If students do not understand these answers, ask, *What was the ticket number on the last ticket that each person sold?* (For Sandra, the last ticket she sold was number 0177, which would result in 200 − 177 = 23 unsold tickets.)

Extension

Ask, *If the highest ticket number sold was 4286, how many packets of tickets were distributed to students?* (If the highest ticket number is 4286, then the last packet distributed contained numbers 4201 to 4300. Each packet contained 100 tickets, so there were 43 packets.)

Working at the Post Office (page 1)

Franklin, Marilyn, and Camilla go to the post office to buy some stamps.

The postal worker shows them a part of a sheet and says, "This is all I have of this stamp. Is this enough?" How many stamps did she show them? Here is their discussion on how to calculate the number of stamps on the sheet.

Franklin:

I would calculate 4 times 10 and then add 3.

Marilyn:

I would calculate 3 times 5, and then 7 times 4, and then add the two answers.

Camilla:

I would calculate 5 times 10, and then subtract 7.

1. Use the pictures of the stamps to explain each strategy.

You can summarize each strategy by writing an expression using parentheses and operation signs. For example, the expression summarizing Franklin's strategy is (4 × 10) + 3.

2. Summarize each of the other two strategies by writing an expression using parentheses and operation signs.

1. Sample explanations for each strategy:

   Franklin: There are four rows of ten stamps each: $4 \times 10 = 40$ There is one row of three stamps left, so add 3: $40 + 3 = 43$

   Marilyn: There are three columns of five each: $3 \times 5 = 15$ There are seven columns of four each: $7 \times 4 = 28$ Add the two answers: $15 + 28 = 43$

   Camilla: I started with the complete sheet of stamps, five rows of ten stamps; $5 \times 10 = 50$ Seven stamps are already sold, so subtract seven: $50 - 7 = 43$

2. Marilyn: $(3 \times 5) + (7 \times 4)$

   Camilla: $(5 \times 10) - 7$

Working at the Post Office (page 2)

3. Write how you would find the total number of stamps in each set. Summarize your strategy by writing an expression using parentheses and operation signs.

a.

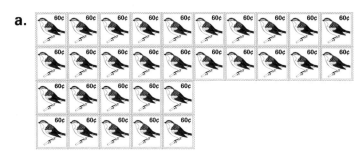

b.

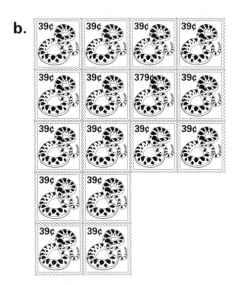

c.

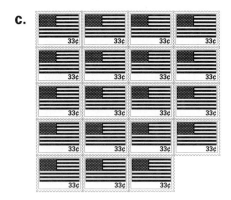

4. Find a new strategy to calculate the stamp sets in problem 3. Write a different expression to describe your new strategy.

Sample strategies and expressions:

3a. and **4a.**

- Five columns of four stamps each (5×4) and five columns of two stamps each (5×2);

  $(5 \times 4) + (5 \times 2) =$

  $20 + 10 = 30$

- Two rows of ten stamps each (2×10) and two rows of five stamps each (2×5)

  $(2 \times 10) + (2 \times 5) =$

  $20 + 10 = 30$

- Four rows of ten stamps (4×10), 10 stamps are already sold

  $(4 \times 10) - 10 =$

  $40 - 10 = 30$

3b. and **4b.**

- Two columns of five stamps each (2×5) and two columns of three stamps each (2×3);

  $(2 \times 5) + (2 \times 3) =$

  $10 + 6 = 16$

- Three rows of four stamps each (3×4) and two rows of two stamps each (2×2)

  $(3 \times 4) + (2 \times 2) =$

  $12 + 4 = 16$

- Five rows of four stamps each (5×4) and four stamps are already sold;

  $(5 \times 4) - 4 =$

  $20 - 4 = 16$

3c. and **4c.**

- Four rows of four stamps each (4×4) and one row of three

  $(4 \times 4) + 1 \times 3 =$

  $16 + 3 = 19$

- Five rows of four stamps each (5×4) and one is already sold;

  $(5 \times 4) - 1 =$

  $20 - 1 = 19$

Costs (page 1)

1. When Mr. Lee buys stamps, he pays with bills and never carries coins or plastic. Estimate how much money Mr. Lee will give the postal worker to purchase each of the following sets of stamps.

a.

c.

b.

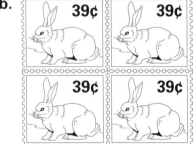

d.

1. a. $2. Sample estimation strategy:

Four 23¢ stamps are about one dollar. There are 2 groups of 4, so Mr. Lee would need to give the clerk $2 to purchase these 8 stamps.

b. $2. Sample estimation strategy:

I considered four 30¢ stamps and four 40¢ stamps. $4 \times 30 = 120$; $4 \times 40 = 160$, so if Mr. Lee gives the clerk $2 it will be more than enough to purchase the four stamps.

c. $4. Sample estimation strategy:

10 stamps would be $3.30, but there are 11 stamps. Mr. Lee needs to give the clerk $4.

d. $2. Sample estimation strategy:

I considered five 40¢ stamps. $5 \times 40 = 200$. Mr. Lee needs to give the clerk $2.

Costs (page 2)

2. Here are sets of stamps that people can buy at the post office. Calculate the cost without the use of a calculator.

   a. 39¢ stamps, featuring American Indian artifacts, available in a sheet of 10. Cost:

   b. Lewis and Clark 39¢ stamps in a book of 20. Cost:

   c. Cloudscapes 39¢ stamps, in a sheet of 15. Cost:

   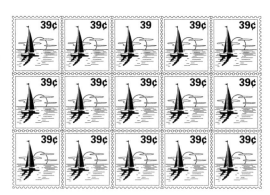

   d. How can you use the answer for problem **a** to find the cost in **b**?

   e. How can you use the answer for problem **a** to find the cost in **c**?

2. a. Cost \$3.90; 10×39

    b. Cost \$7.80; 20×39

        $20 \times (30 + 9) =$

        $(20 \times 30) + (20 \times 9) =$

        $600 + 180 = 780$

    c. Cost \$5.85; $15 \times 39 =$

        $(10 + 5) \times 39 =$

        $(10 \times 39) + (5 \times 39) =$

        $390 + 195 = 585$

        Note: 5×39 is half of 10×39.

    d. You can use the answer of problem **a** by doubling it to find the answer to problem **b**. $20 \times 39 = 2 \times (10 \times 39)$; $2 \times \$3.90 = \$7.80$.

    e. You can use the answer of problem **a**, taking one and one-half of **a**.

        You know 10 stamps cost \$3.90.

        One half of 390 is one half of 300 (or 150) and one half of 90 (or 45); $150 + 45 = 195$.

        Finding one and one half is $390 + \mathbf{195}$; $390 + \mathbf{100} = 490$; $490 + \mathbf{90} = 580$ and $580 + \mathbf{5} = 585$.

        Note that a variety of strategies can be used to solve the problems on this page.

Costs (page 3)

3. For each of the following sets, calculate the cost without using a calculator or pencil and paper. Then show how you mentally calculated the answer.

a.
Wilma Rudolph
23¢ stamps, in a book of 10

Cost:

Mental steps:

b.
George Washington
23¢ stamps, in a book of 20

Cost:

Mental steps:

c.
Love Special
60¢ stamps, in a sheet of 20

Cost:

Mental steps:

d.
Antique Toys
39¢ stamps, in a roll of 100

Cost:

Mental steps:

e.
Greetings From America
Sheet of 50 Self-Adhesive 39¢

Cost:

Mental steps:

f.
American Indian Artifacts
39¢ stamps in a pack of
5 books of 20 stamps

Cost:

Mental steps:

Mental steps may vary. One sample strategy is shown for each problem.

3. a. Cost: $2.30 Mental steps: $(10 \times 20) +$
   $(10 \times 3) = 200 + 30$

b. Cost: $4.60 Mental steps: 20 23¢-stamps is double the cost of ten stamps;
   $2 \times \$2.30 = \$4.60$

c. Cost: $12 Mental steps:
   10 stamps cost $10 \times \$0.60 = \$6$.
   20 stamps are double the cost of ten stamps; $2 \times \$6 = \$12$

d. Cost: $39 Mental steps: $100 \times \$0.39 = \$39$

e. Cost: $18.50 Mental steps:
   50 39¢-stamps is half of 100 39¢-stamps.
   Half of $39 is half of $30 and half of $9;
   $\$15 + \$4.50 = \$19.50$

f. Cost: $39 Mental steps: Five books of 20 stamps each is 100 stamps.
   $100 \times \$0.39 = \$39$

The Goal Game

Simone secretly entered exactly five keystrokes on her calculator. She writes down the buttons she pressed, but not the order she pressed them.

1 **2** **2** **3** **x**

After she presses the = button, she shows everyone her calculator display. It shows the number 636.

1. What is the order Simone pressed the buttons? There are two ways that produce an answer of 636.

You have just played the Goal Game. Simone was the goalkeeper. She wrote down the five buttons she used and showed the answer on her calculator display. The answer displayed is the Goal Number. You had to figure out the order she used. If you match the Goal Number within two minutes, you score a goal for one point.

2. Play the Goal Game in pairs or small groups.

Game rules

- Use any five of these calculator buttons:

1 **2** **3** **4** **5** **6** **7** **8** **9** **0** **+** **x**

To prepare:

The goalkeeper secretly uses his or her calculator to record the 5 buttons and make the Goal Number answer appear in the calculator displays. (The goalkeeper might also make a secret record of the order of the keystrokes.)

To play:

The goalkeeper writes the five buttons and shows the Goal Number to the players. The goalkeeper begins timing for two minutes.

At the end of two minutes, players show their calculator display. If a player matches the Goal Number, that player must recreate the order of the keystrokes for the group. Players recreating the Goal Number score a goal and earn one point. Each player takes a turn being the goalkeeper.

The winner:

The winner is the player who earns the most points after everyone has a turn being the goalkeeper.

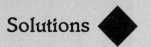
1. There are two ways Simone could press the buttons: $212 \times 3 =$ or $3 \times 212 =$.

Note: You may want to be the goalkeeper to begin the game. Then have students form small groups when they understand how to play.

In order for the game to be fair, each student must be the goalkeeper an equal number of times. You might set the number of rounds at twice the number of players.

Advise students to write down their steps when they are goalkeepers so that they can show how they reached their goal numbers. Also, make sure that students are aware that the "=" button will always be the last button used.

Extension

Allow students to use more than five keystrokes, or have students use an unspecified number of strokes.

Shoveling Sidewalks

On days when it snows, Raúl and his friends shovel their neighbors' sidewalks. For each different day below, color the part of the sidewalks each person shovels. Assume the people shovel equal amounts and that the group shovels all the sidewalks shown. Use fractions to describe the part of a sidewalk each helper shovels.

Day	Sidewalks	Raúl and his friends

1. Each helper shovels:

2. Each helper shovels:

3. Each helper shovels:

4. Each helper shovels:
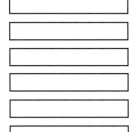

Some possibilities are shown below.

1. Strategy 1   Strategy 2

$\frac{1}{3}$ of a sidewalk $\frac{1}{6} + \frac{1}{6}$ or $2 \times \frac{1}{6}$ of a sidewalk

2. Strategy 1   Strategy 2   Strategy 3

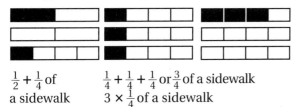

$\frac{1}{2} + \frac{1}{4}$ of $\frac{1}{4} + \frac{1}{4} + \frac{1}{4}$ or $\frac{3}{4}$ of a sidewalk
a sidewalk $3 \times \frac{1}{4}$ of a sidewalk

3. Strategy 1   Strategy 2

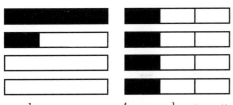

$1 + \frac{1}{3}$ sidewalks $\frac{4}{3}$ or $4 \times \frac{1}{3}$ sidewalks

4. Strategy 1   Strategy 2

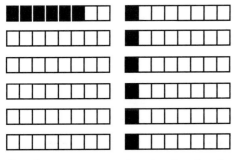

$\frac{6}{8}$ or $\frac{3}{4}$ $\frac{1}{8} + \frac{1}{8} + \frac{1}{8} + \frac{1}{8} + \frac{1}{8} + \frac{1}{8}$
a sidewalk   or $6 \times \frac{1}{8}$ of a sidewalk

Have students share their strategies and compare the different fractions as they answer each problem. If you have students present their solutions on an overhead projector, prepare for multiple solutions by having extra sets of rectangles on transparency sheets.

Possible topics for class discussion:

- equivalent fractions
- relationship between the number of sidewalks and number of sharers.

Extension

Ask students to solve problems 1–4 with one more or one fewer person shoveling.

Modeling Clay

Mike, Liz, and Jordan want to share this bar of modeling clay.

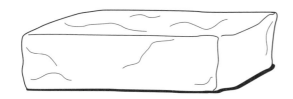

1. Make a drawing of the bar and shade one person's share. Write one person's share as a fraction of the bar.

2. For each example below, write a fraction to represent the part of the bar that is shaded.

a. _____   k. _____

b. _____   l. _____

c. _____   m. _____

d. _____   n. _____

e. _____   o. _____

f. _____   p. _____

g. _____   q. _____

h. _____   r. _____

i. _____   s. _____

j. _____   t. _____

Mathematics in Context

1.

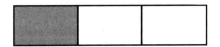

Each person will get $\frac{1}{3}$ of the bar.

2. a. $\frac{1}{6}$ **k.** $\frac{1}{2}$

    b. $\frac{1}{2}$ **l.** $\frac{1}{3}$

    c. $\frac{1}{4}$ **m.** $\frac{2}{3}$

    d. $\frac{1}{8}$ **n.** $\frac{1}{6}$

    e. $\frac{3}{8}$ **o.** $\frac{1}{3}$

    f. $\frac{5}{8}$ **p.** $\frac{1}{2}$

    g. $\frac{3}{8}$ **q.** $\frac{5}{6}$

    h. $\frac{2}{3}$ **r.** $\frac{1}{12}$

    i. $\frac{5}{6}$ **s.** $\frac{6}{12}$ or $\frac{1}{2}$

    j. $\frac{3}{4}$ **t.** $\frac{8}{12}$ or $\frac{2}{3}$

Topics for discussion:

- equivalent fractions
- relationships between one-half, one-fourth and one-eighth
- relationships between one-third and one-sixth
- relationships between complementary fractions; one-third and two-thirds or five-sixths and one-sixth

Measuring Cups

Use an arrow to indicate the level of each measuring cup after the ingredients have been added.

Here you see an example showing that the level of the liquid is $\frac{1}{2}$ cup.

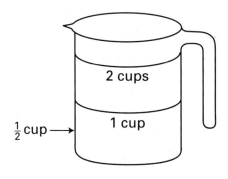

1.

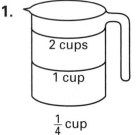

$\frac{1}{4}$ cup

2.

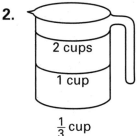

$\frac{1}{3}$ cup

3.

$\frac{2}{3}$ cup

4.

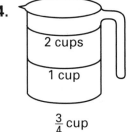

$\frac{3}{4}$ cup

5.

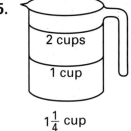

$1\frac{1}{4}$ cup

6.

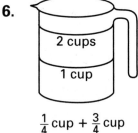

$\frac{1}{4}$ cup + $\frac{3}{4}$ cup

7.

$\frac{2}{3}$ cup + $\frac{2}{3}$ cup

8.

$\frac{3}{4}$ cup + $\frac{1}{2}$ cup

9.

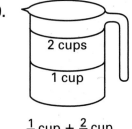

$\frac{1}{2}$ cup + $\frac{2}{3}$ cup

Pictures will vary. Accept answers that are reasonably close to the following.

1.
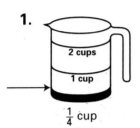
$\frac{1}{4}$ cup

2.
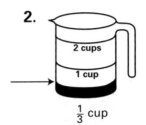
$\frac{1}{3}$ cup

3.
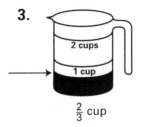
$\frac{2}{3}$ cup

4.
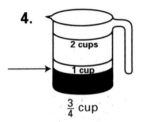
$\frac{3}{4}$ cup

5.
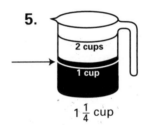
$1\frac{1}{4}$ cup

6.
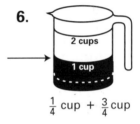
$\frac{1}{4}$ cup $+$ $\frac{3}{4}$ cup

7.
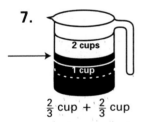
$\frac{2}{3}$ cup $+$ $\frac{2}{3}$ cup

8.
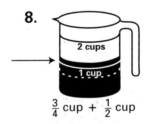
$\frac{3}{4}$ cup $+$ $\frac{1}{2}$ cup

9.
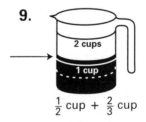
$\frac{1}{2}$ cup $+$ $\frac{2}{3}$ cup

The Jump, Jump Game (page 1)

Object of the Game:

Use a number line to "jump" from one number to another in as *few jumps as possible*. Compare your score with a partner.

To Play:

To get to a number, you can make *jumps of only three lengths: 1, 10, and 100.* You can show your jumps on the number line by drawing curves of different lengths: a small curve for a jump length of 1, a medium curve for a jump length of 10, and a large curve for a jump length of 100. You can jump forward or backward.

For Example: **Jump from 0 to 26**.

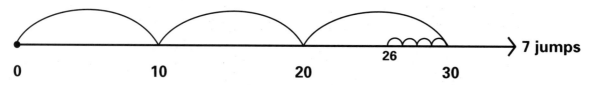

Complete Rounds 1 and 2 individually. After each round, write the total number of jumps you made next to each number line.

Round 1. Jump from 0 to 53.

Round 2. Jump from 0 to 29.

Compare your results with a partner.
Score two points for a win and one point for a tie.

SCORE (1–2)

Do the following rounds individually.
Round 3. Jump from 0 to 69.

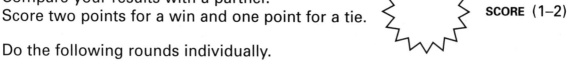

Round 4. Jump from 0 to 83.

Mathematics in Context

The Jump, Jump Game (page 1)

Remind students to clearly distinguish between the different size jumps on their number line. This game will help students combine numbers more efficiently. By moving from one number to another in the fewest jumps and by jumping only 1 space, 10 spaces, or 100 spaces at a time, students build on their sense of numbers.

Encourage students to use their number line to talk about how they jumped.

Sample explanation for jumping from 17 to 36:

Starting at 17, I would make one 10-jump to get to 27, another 10-jump to get to 37, but I need to go back 1 small jump to end up at 36. So I can do it in 3 jumps.

This means that $36 - 17 = 19$ ($19 = 2 \times 10 - 1$).
It also means $17 + 19 = 36$.

Being able to add ten to a number like 17 is a milestone for young math students. Hopefully your students feel comfortable adding 10 and 100 to non-decade numbers like 17. Initially students might only feel comfortable adding 10 and 100 to decade numbers like 60.

One possibility is given for each problem below, showing the minimum number of jumps required.

1. 8 jumps with target of 53

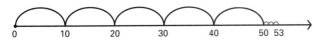

5 jumps to 50 and 3 small jumps to 53

2. 4 jumps with target of 29

3 jumps to 30 and 1 small jump back to 29

3. 5 jumps, with a target of 69

1 100-jump, 3 10-jumps back to 70, and 1 small jump back to 69.

4. 6 jumps with a target of 83

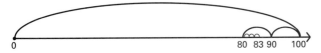

1 100-jump, 2 10-jumps back to 80, and 3 small jumps right to 83

The Jump, Jump Game (page 2)

Round 5. Jump from 0 to 57.

0

Compare your results with a partner.
Score two points for a win and one point for a tie.

SCORE

The next few rounds are a little different. Complete them individually.

Round 6. Jump from 4 to 79.

Round 7. Jump from 45 to 87.

Round 8. Jump from 56 to 173.

Round 9. Jump from 324 to 546.

Round 10. Jump from 1492 to the current year.

Winner: _____

Winning Score: _____

TOTAL SCORE
(0–10)

5. 8 jumps with a target of 57

1 100-jump, 4 10-jumps back to 60, and 3 small jumps back to 57

Extension

Ask students to generate one number sentence for each number line.

6. 8 jumps, from 4 to a target of 79

1 100-jump to 104, 2 10-jumps back to 84, and 5 small jumps back to 79, (4 to 80 and 1 more to 79).

$79 - 4 = 100 - 20 - 5 = 75$

7. 6 jumps, from 45 to 87.

4 10-jumps to 85 and 2 small jumps to 87.

$87 - 45 = 4 \times 10 + 2 = 42$

8. 6 jumps, from 56 to 173

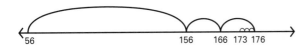

1 100-jump to 156, 2 10-jumps to 176, and 3 small jumps back to 173

$173 - 56 = 100 + 2 \times 10 - 3 = 117$

9. 6 jumps from 324 to 546

2 100-jumps to 524, 2 10-jumps to 544, and 2 small jumps to 546

$546 - 324 = 2 \times 100 + 2 \times 10 + 2 = 222$

10. For year 2005, 9 jumps. Answers will depend on the current year.

5 jumps of 100 to 1992, one jump of 10 to 2002, and 3 small jumps to 2005.

$1492 + 5 \times 100 + 10 + 3 = 2005$

On the Number Line

A group of students has a paper airplane contest.
The Distance List shows the flight distance for each
person's airplane. The distance is measured
along the ground in centimeters.

Distance List—Round 1	
Student	**Flight Distance (in cm)**
Jim	244
Shantha	367
Lester	120
Giorgio	167
Bido	250
Alice	203
Arba	278
Martha	385

1. Locate the numbers for the flight distances on
this number line. Reasonable estimates will do.

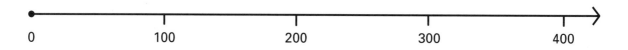

Length of Flight (in cm)

The students organized a second round. This number
line shows the results of the second round.

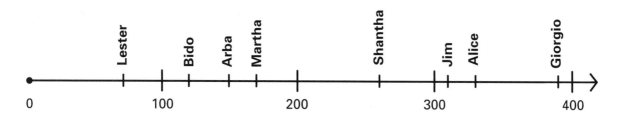

2. Use the number line to fill in the Distance List
for Round 2. Reasonable estimates will do.
Who is the winner after both rounds?
Explain how you decided.

Distance List—Round 2	
Student	**Flight Distance (in cm)**
Jim	_____
Shantha	_____
Lester	_____
Giorgio	_____
Bido	_____
Alice	_____
Arba	_____
Martha	_____

The problems on this page give students practice locating numbers on the number line. Students will need to estimate where numbers would appear on the number line. For example, 48 is close to 50 but a little to the left of it.

1. Answers may vary but should be close to the approximations given below:

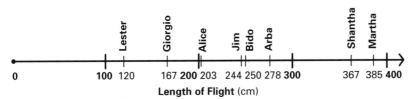

Length of Flight (cm)

2. Answers will vary but should be close to the approximations given below:

Distance List—Round 2	
Student	**Flight Distance (in cm)**
Jim	310 cm
Shantha	260 cm
Lester	70 cm
Giorgio	390 cm
Bido	120 cm
Alice	330 cm
Arba	150 cm
Martha	170 cm

Answers and explanations will vary.

Sample responses:

- Georgio is winner, because he had the farthest distance of both rounds.
- If you add the scores for each round, at the end of two rounds Jim, Georgio and Martha are very close together but Georgio is ahead by 2 cm, so he is winner.

Extension

Ask students whether or not a number line always has to start at zero. Ask, *Can you think of any situations in which it would be simpler to use a number line that does not start at zero?* (Students might say that they would not need the zero if they were graphing the ages of only their parents. Then a more appropriate number line might start at 25 and continue on to 65, with arrows on each end showing that the number line could be extended to include ages less than 25 or greater than 65.)

The Number Line as a Tool (page 1)

Suppose you work at a booth selling beads. A customer wants to buy 29 brown beads and 67 amber-colored beads. All the beads sell for 10 cents each.

1. Find the total cost. Show your work.

2. There are different strategies to find the total number of beads. The number lines below show three strategies. Below each number line, describe the strategy shown.

a.

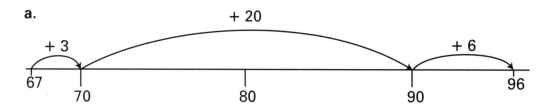

b.

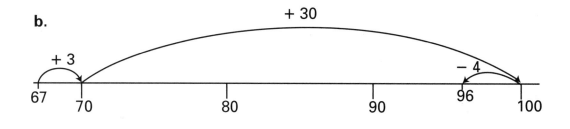

c.

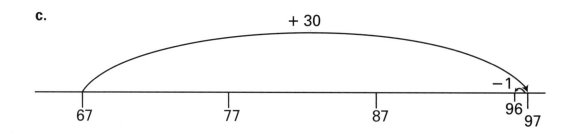

3. Use the number line below to show your strategy for adding 67 beads to 29 beads; start with 29 beads.

29

1. There are 96 beads and at 10 cents apiece, the cost is $9.60

   Note: You might save the discussion of this problem until after you have discussed problems 2 and 3. As students present their strategies, ask them to identify which strategy closely resembles their strategy.

2. **a.** Starting with the larger number 67, she added a total of 29 beads; 3 beads more to get to the decade number (70), 20 to more (to 90) and then 6 more to finish adding all 29 beads. She ends up at 96.

   b. Starting with the larger number 67, he kept track to add a total of 29 beads; 3 beads more to get to the decade number (70), 30 more (to 100), and compensating by taking away 4 beads (to 96), because he really added 33 beads, and he was only supposed to add 29.

   c. Starting with the larger number 67, he added 30 beads and took 1 back to add a total of 29 beads ($67 + 30 - 1 = 96$).

   Students identify their chosen strategy. Have them explain why they prefer this strategy.

3. Three different number lines:

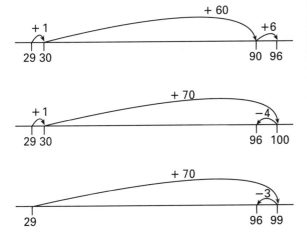

Extension

Ask students which number is easier to start with. Why is this possible? (Addition is commutative; you can add two numbers in any order and get the same result.)

The Number Line as a Tool (page 2)

Draw a number line to show how you would solve each
problem mentally. Explain your solution.

Mira's necklace has 18 beads. Nancy's necklace has 75 beads
more than Mira's.

4. How many beads does Nancy's necklace have?

Julie buys a package of beads for $2.10 and a cord for $0.98.

5. a. What is the total cost for Julie's items?

b. Julie pays with a 10-dollar bill. How much change
does she receive?

Mathematics in Context

4. Nancy's necklace has 93 beads. Sample strategies:

Strategy 1

Since Mira has 18 beads and Nancy has 75 beads more than Mira, I can count on from 18 by tens (28, 38, 48, 58, 68, 78, 88) until I have added 70. Then I add five more to get 93.

Strategy 2

Start with 75, add 20, and then subtract two so that the net result is 75 plus 18 (93).

Note: This second strategy is a compensation strategy. The compensation method uses the idea that it is easier to add on a rounded number and then compensate for the rounding at the end.
For example, to use the compensation strategy for 17 + 19, students might round 19 up by 1 to 20,
then add 17 + 20, and then subtract one.
A number sentence illustrating this strategy is $17 + 19 = 17 + 20 - 1$.

5. a. The total cost for the two items is $3.08. ($2.10 + $0.98 = $2.10 + $1.00 − $0.02). One sample strategy is shown below:

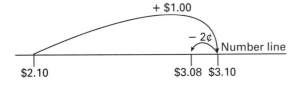

I started with $2.10 and added $1, which results in $3.10. Then I subtracted the two cents because I needed to add $0.98 and not $1.

5. b. Julia's change is $6.92.

Sample strategies:

- Go from $3.08 to $10 and add up the jumps. ($10.00 − 3.08 = $0.02 + $0.90 + $6.00)

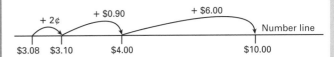

I made jumps from $3.08 to $10, and then added all the amounts at the arrows:

$2¢ + $0.90 + $6.00 = 6.92

- Start at $10 and make jumps that represent "take away $3.08." Where you end is the answer.

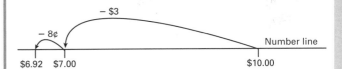

I subtracted $3 from $10, which results in $7. Then I subtracted 8 cents because I had to subtract $3.08.

The Number Line as a Tool (page 3)

Each morning Hasan rides his bike 7.4 miles to school, and Jerret rides his bike 3.8 miles.

6. Compared to Jerret, how much farther does Hasan ride his bike to school?

Gwen and Gordon ride along a bike trail that is 36.4 miles long. Gwen's bike computer shows that they have already ridden their bikes 15.8 miles.

7. If they plan to ride the complete trail, how many more miles will they ride their bikes?

Solve the following problems mentally. It may be helpful to make a mental model of the number line.

8. Jonathan is having a party for a few of his closest friends. The catering bill comes to $249. He decides to give a $38 tip. How much money does he give the caterers in total?

9. At a track meet, Lisa jumped 652 centimeters in the long jump competition, Shelice jumped 595 centimeters. Compared to Shelice, how much farther did Lisa jump?

10. Create and solve your own problem using the numbers 508 and 470.

6. Hasan has to ride his bike 3.6 more miles than Jerret.

Sample strategies:

- Go from 3.8 to 7.8 and add the jumps.

$$3.8 + 4 - 0.4 = 7.4$$
$$3.8 + 3.6 = 7.4$$

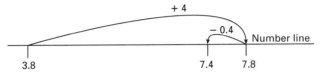

4 to the right and 0.4 to the left is the same as 3.6 to the right.

- Start at 7.8 and make jumps that represent "take away 3.8." Where you end is the answer.

$$7.8 - 3.8 =$$
$$7.8 - 4 + 0.2 = 3.6$$

7. They still have to go 20.6 miles. Sample strategies:

- Go from 15.8 to 36.4 and add the jumps.

$$15.8 + 0.6 + 20 = 36.4$$
$$15.8 + 20.6 = 36.4$$

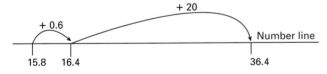

Total of the jumps is $0.6 + 20 = 20.6$

- Start at 36.4 and make jumps that represent "take away 15.8." Where you end is the answer.

$$36.4 - 15.8 =$$
$$36.4 - 16 + 0.2 = 20.6$$

8. Total bill is $287. Sample strategy:

$249 + 1 + 250$ (one step of one on the number line)

$250 + 30 = 280$ (three steps of ten on the number line)

$280 + 7 = 287$ (seven steps of one on the number line)

9. Lisa jumped 57 cm farther than Shelice. Sample strategies:

$595 + 5 = 600$ (I added 5 in total.)

$600 + 50 = 650$ (I added 55 in total.)

$650 + 2 = 652$ (I added 57 in total.)

I know that $652 - 600 = 52$ and that $600 - 595 = 5$, so I figured $52 + 5 = 57$

10. Sample problem:

The school purchased 508 sports banners, one for each student. They distributed 470 banners at the pep rally. How many banners were left over?

Answer: 38 banners were left.

Sample strategy using addition:

$470 + 30 = 500$ (I added 30.)

$500 + 8 = 508$ (I added 8.)

Sample strategy using subtraction:

$508 - 8 = 500$ (I subtracted 8.)

$500 - 30 = 470$ (I subtracted 30.)

Note: It may be helpful for students to share their strategies because they may have used different mental models to solve the problems.

At the Cash Register

Imagine that you are the cashier at a store. Customers give you money to pay for their purchases. You have to give them change. When you make change, hand back the fewest bills and coins possible.

1. For each purchase, give change to each customer. Use tally marks to show how much of each coin and/or bill you would return to each customer. As an example, change for a purchase of $13.49 when the customer pays with a twenty-dollar bill is one penny, two quarters, one one-dollar bill, and one five-dollar bill.

Purchase	Payment	Change—Fewest Coin and Bills								
		1¢	5¢	10¢	25¢	$1	$5	$10	$20	$50
$13.49	$20.00	I			II	I	I			
$67.88	$100.00									
$198.21	$200.01									
$23.02	$100.02									

Now imagine that you are the customer.

2. For each purchase, write how much you would give a cashier. Then use tally marks to show how much of each coin/bill you expect as change.

Purchase	Payment	Change—Fewest Coin and Bills								
		1¢	5¢	10¢	25¢	$1	$5	$10	$20	$50
$5.98	$_____									
$16.23	$_____									
$59.80	$_____									
$5.08	$_____									

Mathematics in Context

1.

Purchase	Payment	Change—Fewest Coin and Bills								
		1¢	5¢	10¢	25¢	$1	$5	$10	$20	$50
$13.49	$20.00	/			//	/	/			
$67.88	$100.00	//		/		//		/	/	
$198.21	$200.01		/		///	/				
$23.02	$100.02					//	/		/	/

2. Students answers will depend upon the Payment amount they choose. Sample work from one student:

Purchase	Payment	Change—Fewest Coin and Bills								
		1¢	5¢	10¢	25¢	$1	$5	$10	$20	$50
$5.98	$10.00	//				////				
$16.23	$20.00	//			///	///				
$59.80	$100.00			//					//	
$5.08	$50.00	//	/	/	///	////			//	

Note: Allow students to choose numbers with which they feel comfortable. Some will choose numbers that make the calculations easy, while others will want a challenge.

The Vending Machine

How many quarters, dimes, and/or nickels do you have to
put into this vending machine to get the following items?
Record at least five possible coin combinations for each
item. As an example, two of the five combinations for
item **a** are listed in the table.

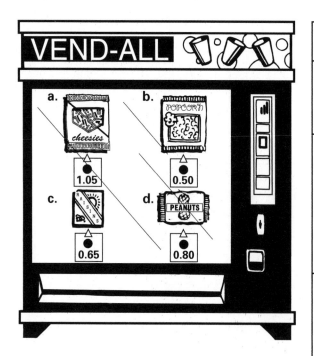

ITEM	Five different possible coin combinations to Purchase each Item		
	quarters	dimes	nickels
a.	4	0	1
	2	5	1
	3	....	....
b.			
c.			
d.			

Five combinations are listed in the table; other coin combinations are possible. Verify that the coins match the total price of each item.

Item/Price	quarters	dimes	nickels
Five different possible coin combinations to Purchase each Item			
a. $1.05	4	0	1
	2	5	1
	3	3	0
	1	8	0
	0	10	1
b. $0.50	2	0	0
	1	2	1
	0	5	0
	0	4	2
	0	3	4
c. $0.65	2	1	1
	1	4	0
	1	3	2
	0	6	1
	0	5	3
d. $0.80	3	0	1
	2	3	0
	2	0	6
	1	5	1
	0	0	16

Note: Encourage students to organize their work while finding combinations. For example, start with the largest number of quarters and then to the largest number of dimes, and so on.

Extension

- Ask students to find patterns in the tables.

  One pattern is that when the number of dimes decreases by 1, the number of nickels increases by 2.

  Another pattern is that when the price is even, the number of quarters plus the number of nickels is also even. When the price is odd, the number of quarters plus the number of nickels is odd.

- Ask students to generate all the combinations. How do they know they have them all?

  a. 31 possible coin combinations,

  b. 10 possibilities,

  c. 14 possibilities,

  d. 20 possibilities

Checking the Bill

1. Patricia received this restaurant bill.

After quickly checking the bill, Patricia knew the waiter made an addition error. Explain how she knew the addition was wrong even though she did not perform an exact calculation.

Check	
~~	$6.98
~~	$7.98
~~	$4.25
~~	$6.96
~~	$2.00
~~	$3.00
Total	$41.17

Thank You

2. Here are some receipts from shopping trips to the supermarket. Quickly estimate the total for each receipt and explain how you estimated.

a.

$3.98
$3.98
$3.98
$3.98
$3.98

Total _____

b.

$2.97
$3.06
$5.99
$0.99

Total _____

c.

$0.75
$0.75
$0.75
$0.75
$0.75
$0.75
$0.75
$0.75

Total _____

d.

$0.24
$0.24
$0.24
$0.24
$0.24
$0.24
$0.24

Total _____

e.

$5.96
$2.96
$4.96
$3.96
$5.96

Total _____

f.

$5.98
$9.02
$6.97
$3.03
$4.02
$2.98

Total _____

g.

$3.31
$2.58
$6.49
$2.65
$5.38
$0.44

Total _____

h.

$6.38
$4.12
$9.72
$4.08
$5.74
$2.68

Total _____

3. Compare your estimates with a classmate. Describe a way you can improve your estimation skills.

1. Sample explanation:

   Patricia might have rounded the prices to dollars and then added: $7 + 8 + 4 + 7 + 2 + 3 = 31$. This answer is not even close to $41.

2. Sample estimates and the corresponding estimation strategies:

   a. $20

   I rounded $3.98 to $4 and multiplied by 5; $5 \times \$4 = \$20$.

   b. $13

   I rounded each price to dollars and added; $3 + 3 + 6 + 1 = 13$.

   c. $6

   2 groups of $0.75 is $1.50, 4 groups is $3.00, so 8 groups is $6.00.

   I know that $0.75 is $\frac{3}{4}$ of a dollar, and since there are 8 of these, I can find $\frac{3}{4}$ of $8, which is $6.

   d. $1.75

   I rounded $0.24 to $0.25 (one quarter), and counted 7 items;

   $7 \times \$0.25 = \$1.75$ (seven quarters).

   e. $24

   I rounded each price to dollars and added; $(6 + 3 + 5 + 4 + 6 = 24)$.

   f. $32

   I rounded each price to dollars and added; $(6 + 9 + 7 + 3 + 4 + 3 = 32)$.

   g. $21

   First I added just the dollar amounts; $3 + 2 + 6 + 2 + 5 = 18$.

   Then I rounded the decimal amounts to 50¢ and counted 6; $6 \times 50¢ = \$3.00$

   Combining both; ($18 + $3 = $21).

   h. $33

   First I added just the dollar amounts; $(6 + 4 + 9 + 4 + 5 + 2 = 30)$.

   Then I rounded the decimal amounts and added; $(40¢ + 10¢ + 70¢ + 10¢ + 70¢ + 70¢ \approx \$3)$. Combining both; ($30 + $3 = $33).

3. Answers will vary depending on the strategies used by the students

Note: Discuss different estimation strategies. Because the numbers for these problems are listed in columns, students may be tempted to calculate instead of estimate. One important distinction between the calculating and estimating is that when estimating, you usually work from left to right, starting with the largest units and rounding the smaller units. When calculating, you work from right to left, starting with the smallest units.

Collecting Pennies

Here is a penny-collecting tube. The tube is completely full when it contains 100 pennies ($1.00).

1. Draw a line to show the height of the tube if it contained each of these amounts of money. Write the corresponding letter next to each height. As an example, problem **a** has been done for you.

a. $0.25   **h.** $0.80

b. $0.50   **i.** $0.98

c. $0.75   **j.** $0.09

d. $0.20   **k.** $1.00

e. $0.02   **l.** $0.10

f. $0.77   **m.** $0.67

g. $0.40

2. Draw an arrow to connect each decimal number to its unique place on the number line.

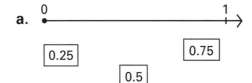

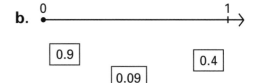

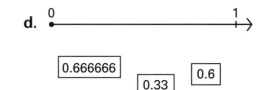

1.

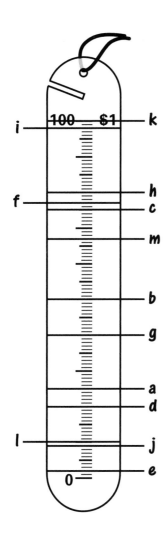

2.

a.

b.

c.
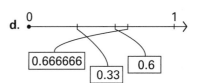

d.
0 ————————————— 1

| 0.666666 | | 0.6 |

0.33

Summer Camp

Ms. Lampert organizes a summer camp for children. This year, 169 children have signed up for camp. Ms. Lampert needs to figure out how many tents will accommodate 169 children. Each tent is large enough for 12 children.

1. **a.** How many tents does Ms. Lampert need? Solve the problem *without using a calculator.* Describe and label how you found your answer as Strategy 1.

   b. Find a classmate who solved the problem using a different strategy. Copy this different strategy as Strategy 2.

This problem can be solved in many different ways. You might have written down all of the steps you took to find the answer. Using a **ratio table** is a good way to keep track of all the steps.

With a ratio table, you start with a known ratio (in this case, 1 tent for 12 children) and use it to find other numbers with the same ratio (10 tents for 120 children, for example). You can keep using the numbers you find to discover more numbers until you solve the problem.

Here is how Jamal solved this problem using a ratio table.

Tents	1	10	5	15	14
Children	12	120	60	180	168

2. Explain how Jamal found the numbers in each new column.

3. Explain how Jamal will use his ratio table to answer the question. (How many tents does Ms. Lampert need to accommodate 169 children?)

1. Ms. Lampert needs 15 tents. Sample strategies:

- I counted by 12s until I got enough for 169 children; 12, 24, 36, 48, 60, 72, 84, 96, 108, 120, 132, 144, 156, 168, 180. The first number over 169 is 180. I had to count by 12 fifteen times to get to 180, so the answer is 15.

- I know that $12 \times 12 = 144$, so 12 tents are not enough; 12×13 is 12 more than 12×12 ($144 + 12 = 156$), but 156 is still not enough. 12×14 is 168, which also is not enough, but 12 times 15 is 180, so 15 tents must be enough for 169 people.

2. First column: 1 tent can hold 12 children

Second column: multiply both numbers of the 1st column by ten

Third column: divide both numbers in the previous column by 2

Fourth column: multiply both numbers in the previous column by 3

Fifth column: subtract the numbers in the first column from those in the fourth column

3. Sample explanation:

In the last column of the ratio table, you found that 14 tents can hold 168 children. However, there are 169 children, so one extra tent is needed. Ms. Lampert needs 15 tents.

Note: Students should recognize that several different strategies lead to the same solution. They should also recognize the usefulness of the ratio table—it is a concise, organized way to keep track of your calculations.

Bottles (page 1)

1. Camp's juice cases contain 15 bottles of juice. Use the
   following ratio tables to find out how many bottles
   there are in different numbers of cases:

   a. 8 cases

Cases	1	2	4	8				
Bottles	15							

   b. 6 cases

Cases	1	2	3	6				
Bottles	15							

   c. 15 cases

Cases	1	10	5	15				
Bottles	15							

   d. 9 cases

Cases	1	10	9					
Bottles	15							

   e. 99 cases

Cases	1							
Bottles	15							

2. Jake wants 155 bottles of Camp's juice. Use the following
   ratio table to determine how many cases he needs to order.
   Add more columns if necessary.

Cases	1							
Bottles	15							

Note: There are other possible ratio table solutions to these problems. Discuss different strategies with students.

4. a. 120 bottles of juice.

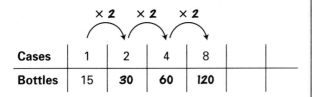

Cases	1	2	4	8		
Bottles	15	30	60	120		

b. 90 bottles of juice.

Cases	1	2	3	6			
Bottles	15	30	45	90			

×2   + col. 1   ×2

c. 225 bottles of juice.

×10   ÷2   ×3

Cases	1	10	5	15			
Bottles	15	150	75	225			

d. 135 bottles of juice.

×10   − column 1

Cases	1	10	9				
Bottles	15	150	135				

e. 1,485 bottles of juice.

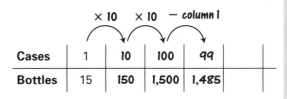

Cases	1	10	100	99	
Bottles	15	150	1,500	1,485	

5. Jake orders 11 cases.

Ten cases are not enough because it will only give him 150 bottles. He wants 155, so one more case will do.

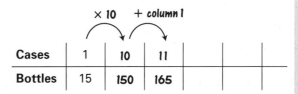

Cases	1	10	11			
Bottles	15	150	165			

Bottles (page 2)

Camp's Beverages sells cases of mineral water and juice.
A full case of mineral water contains 12 bottles.

3. Fill in this ratio table to find out how many bottles
   there are in 24 cases. (You do not have to use all
   columns in the table. You may add more columns
   if you need them.)

Cases	1							
Bottles	12							

Twenty-four cases of Camp's mineral water contain
_____ bottles.

4. Use the ratio table to find out how many bottles there
   are in 31 cases.

   (You may add more columns if you need them. On
   the other hand, you may leave columns blank if you
   do not need them.)

Cases	1							
Bottles	12							

Thirty-one cases of Camp's mineral water contain
_____ bottles.

5. Jake wants 98 bottles of mineral water for an office
   party. How many cases will he order?

Cases	1							
Bottles	12							

For Jake's order of 98 bottles, he will order _____
cases of Camp's mineral water.

1. In 24 cases there are 288 bottles.

Sample ratio table strategy:

		× 10	× 2	÷ 10	× 2	+ column 3
Cases	1	10	20	2	4	24
Bottles	12	120	240	24	48	288

2. In 31 cases there are 372 bottles.

Sample table:

		× 10	× 3	+ column 1
Cases	1	10	30	31
Bottles	12	120	360	372

3. Nine cases

Jake needs to order nine cases. If Jake orders only eight cases, he will need 2 additional bottles of water. Sample table:

		× 2	× 2	× 2
Cases	1	2	4	8
Bottles	12	24	48	96

How Do You Do It? (page 1)

Using ratio tables is a convenient way to solve some problems. You may have discovered that the ratio table offers a handy way to write down the intermediate steps you take to solve a problem.

There are several ways to use existing numbers to find new numbers. Here are some examples of operations you can use.

1. Fill in the missing numbers.

a. Doubling or Multiplying by Two

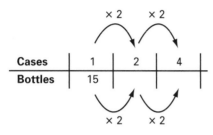

b. Halving or Dividing By Two

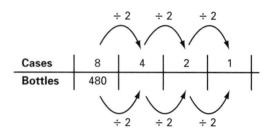

c. Times Ten

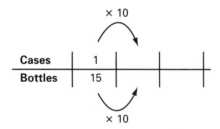

d. Multiplying

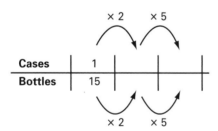

e. Dividing

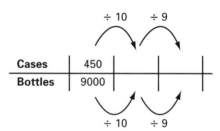

f. Adding Columns

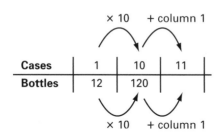

g. Subtracting Columns

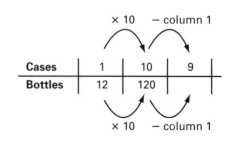

a. Doubling or Multiplying by Two

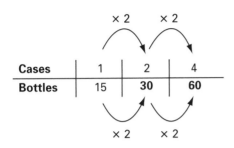

Cases	1	2	4
Bottles	15	**30**	**60**

b. Halving or Dividing by Two

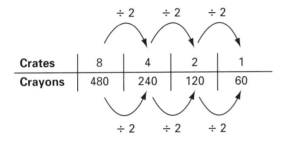

Crates	8	4	2	1
Crayons	480	240	120	60

c. Times Ten

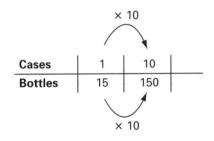

Cases	1	10	
Bottles	15	150	

d. Multiplying

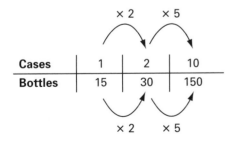

Cases	1	2	10
Bottles	15	30	150

e. Dividing

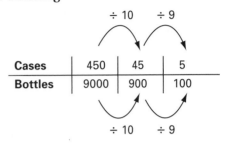

Cases	450	45	5
Bottles	9000	900	100

f. Adding Columns

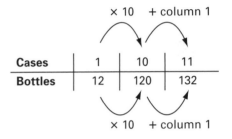

Cases	1	10	11
Bottles	12	120	132

g. Subtracting Columns

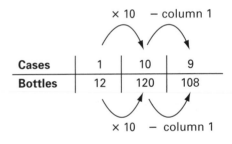

Cases	1	10	9
Bottles	12	120	108

How Do You Do It? (page 2)

Finish the ratio tables below. Circle the operation you used.

2. Anton earns $13 a day at his summer job, baby-sitting his cousins. How much will he earn in 20 days?

Days	1	10	20
Dollars	13	130	

adding • times 10 • doubling
halving • subtracting
multiplying

3. One bottle of apple juice costs $2.75. How much do four bottles of apple juice cost?

Bottles	1	2	4
Dollars	2.75	5.50	

adding • times 10 • doubling
halving • subtracting
multiplying

4. Mr. Pink wants to buy 40 stamps for his office. How much will he pay if each stamp is worth $0.39?

Stamps	1	2	4	40
Dollars	0.39	0.78	1.56	

adding • times 10 • doubling
halving • subtracting
multiplying

5. Altagracia can fill six glasses with one bottle of apple juice. How many glasses can she fill with three bottles?

Bottles	1	3		
Glasses	6			

adding • times 10 • doubling
halving • subtracting
multiplying

On your own:

6. There are 24 bottles in one case. How many bottles are there in nine cases?

Cases	1							
Bottles	24							

2. Anton will earn $260 in 20 days.

Days	1	10	20
Dollars	13	130	260

adding • (times 10) • (doubling)
halving • subtracting
multiplying

3. Four bottles of apple juice cost $11.

Bottles	1	2	4
Dollars	2.75	5.50	11.00

adding • times 10 • (doubling)
halving • subtracting
multiplying

4. 40 stamps cost $15.60.

Stamps	1	2	4	40
Dollars	0.39	0.78	1.56	15.60

adding • (times 10) • (doubling)
halving • subtracting
multiplying

5. Three bottles will fill 18 glasses.

Bottles	1	3
Glasses	6	18

adding • times 10 • doubling
halving • subtracting
(multiplying)

6. There are 216 bottles in 9 cases.

Cases	1	2	4	5	9
Bottles	24	48	96	120	216

(adding) • times 10 • (doubling)
halving • subtracting
multiplying

Note: Discuss the many different solution strategies for problem 6.

Plants I

Two geranium plants cost $1.25.

1. How many plants can you buy for ten dollars?
Show your work.

Here you see how Nadia solved the problem.
She made a mistake somewhere.

Nadia

Plants	2	4	6	8
Dollars	1.25	2.50	5.00	10.00

You can buy eight plants for ten dollars.

2. a. Check each step Nadia made in the ratio table and find where she made the mistake. Then correct her work.

b. How would you explain to Nadia what she did wrong?

Theo solved the following problem:
Three violets cost $1.75. What will 15 violets cost?

Theo

Plants	3	6	12	15
Dollars	1.75	3.50	7.00	10.00

15 violets will cost ten dollars.

Theo also did something wrong.

3. a. Find where he made the mistake and correct his work.

b. How would you explain to Theo what he did wrong?

Mathematics in Context

1. You can buy 16 plants for ten dollars. Sample strategy using a ratio table:

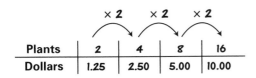

Plants	2	4	8	16
Dollars	1.25	2.50	5.00	10.00

2. a. The first two steps in Nadia's table are right. For the entries in the top row, she added 2 in the last two columns, and in the bottom row she multiplied by 2. A correct table is shown with problem 1.

b. Sample explanation: I would tell Nadia she should be careful of the difference between adding two and multiplying by two. For the number 2 it doesn't make any difference when you add two or multiply it by two, however with larger numbers, there is a huge difference as shown in the two tables.

3. a. Theo made a mistake in the last column. He added 3 in the top row, which is correct, but in the bottom row, he should have added 1.75 instead of 3.

× 2   × 2   + column 1

Plants	3	6	12	15
Dollars	1.75	3.50	7.00	8.75

b. Sample explanation. I would show Theo, by using arrows as in 3.a, that if you add the numbers in the first column to those in the third column, you should add 3 to 12 and 1.75 to 7.00.

Plants II (page 1)

Mr. Martin's biology class is starting a school garden. They will be ordering plants by the box from a nursery. Mr. Martin asked the class to figure out how many tomato plants are in 16 boxes if one box contains 35 plants.

Three students—Darrell, Tasha, and Carla—solved the problem using ratio tables, but each student used a different table.

1. Darrell solved the problem as shown below.
   Explain Darrell's solution.

Boxes	1	2	3	4	5	6	7	8	16
Plants	35	70	105	140	175	210	245	280	560

2. Tasha solved the problem as shown below.
   Explain Tasha's solution.

Boxes	1	2	4	8	16
Plants	35	70	140	280	560

3. Carla solved the problem as shown below.
   Explain Carla's solution.

Boxes	1	10	2	6	16
Plants	35	350	70	210	560

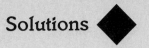
1. Sample explanation: Darrell added one box and 35 plants to each of the columns 1–8 and for the last column multiplied by two to get 16 boxes.

2. Sample explanation: Tasha started by one box and 35 plants and multiplied columns by two until she reached 16. Her solution takes less time than Darrell's.

3. Sample explanation: Carla started by one box and 35 plants. She multiplied the column and got 10 boxes. Then she either divided the second column by 5 or multiplied the first column by 2 to get 2 boxes. She multiplied the third column by 3 and then added the second column plus the fourth column to reach 16 boxes.

Plants II (page 2)

4. Think of your own way to use a ratio table to figure out how many tomato plants are in 16 boxes with 35 tomato plants in each box. Show your solution in the table below. You may add as many columns as you need to the table.

Boxes	1				
Tomato Plants	35				

5. Cactus plants are shipped 45 pots to a box. If Mr. Martin's class orders 360 cactus plants, how many boxes will they get? Show your strategy using the following ratio table.

Boxes						
Cactuses						

6. Mr. Martin's students decide that they need 675 cactus plants. How many boxes will arrive?

Boxes						
Cactuses						

7. Rose bushes are shipped in boxes of 15. Mr. Martin's class orders 255 rose bushes. How many boxes is this?

Boxes					
Roses					

8. Strawberry plants are shipped in boxes of 70. If Mr. Martin's class orders 980 strawberry plants, how many boxes will arrive?

Boxes					
Strawberry Plants					

Note that the tables shown are just examples.
There are other possible solutions. Discuss
different strategies with students.

4. In 16 boxes there are 560 tomato plants.
Sample table:

	×2	×2	×2	×2
Boxes	1	2	4	8	16
Tomato Plants	35	70	140	280	560

5. Mr. Martin's class gets 8 boxes. Sample table:

	×2	×2	×2	
Boxes	1	2	4	8	
Cactuses	45	90	180	360	

6. 15 boxes will arrive. Sample table:

	×2	×2	×2	×2	− column 1
Boxes	1	2	4	8	16	15
Cactuses	45	90	180	360	720	675

7. 17 boxes. Sample tables:

	×2	×2	×2	×2	+ column 1
Boxes	1	2	4	8	16	17
Roses	15	30	60	120	240	255

8. 14 boxes. Sample table:

		×2		
	×10		column 2 + 2 × column 3	
Boxes	1	10	2	14
Strawberry Plants	70	700	140	980

Fruits

In order to solve the problems on this page, you may use the ratio table given with each problem. If necessary, add extra columns.

1. A fruit stand sells three apples for $2. How much would you have to pay for 12 apples?

Apples	3			
Dollars	2.00			

2. What would you have to pay for 33 apples? Choose your own method to calculate the answer.

Apples	3					
Dollars	2.00					

3. The fruit stand sells five California oranges for $3.75. How much would you have to pay for 35 oranges?

Oranges	5			
Dollars	3.75			

4. Four Florida oranges sell for $2.50. You have $10 to spend. How many oranges can you buy?

Oranges	4			
Dollars	2.50			

5. Two cantaloupes sell for $3. How many cantaloupes can you buy for $7.50?

Cantaloupes	2			
Dollars	3.00			

1. $8. Two ratio table strategies:

Apples	3	6	9	12
Dollars	2.00	4.00	6.00	8.00

Apples	3	6	12
Dollars	2.00	4.00	8.00

2. $22. Two ratio table strategies:

Apples	3	12	24	36	33
Dollars	2.00	8.00	16.00	24.00	22.00

Apples	3	30	33		
Dollars	2.00	20.00	22.00		

3. $26.25. Two ratio table strategies:

Oranges	5	10	20	30	35
Dollars	3.75	7.50	15.00	22.50	26.25

Oranges	5	10	20	40	35
Dollars	3.75	7.50	15.00	30.00	26.25

4. 16 oranges. One ratio table strategy:

Oranges	4	8	16
Dollars	2.50	5.00	10.00

5. Five cantaloupes. Two ratio table strategies:

Cantaloupes	2	1	4	5
Dollars	3.00	1.50	6.00	7.50

Cantaloupes	2	10	5
Dollars	3.00	15.00	7.50

Two Steps for Efficiency (page 1)

1. Find the answers to the following problems without using a pencil and paper or a calculator.

   a.   547 + 99 =

   b.   437 + 99 =

   c.   8,035 + 99 =

   d.   63 + 99 =

   e.   21,653 + 99 =

2. Did you discover any shortcuts when you solved problem 1? If so, explain; if not, look back and write about one you could have used.

   Karen has $483 in her savings account. She deposits another $90 into her account and then figures out her total balance.

   The arrow string below shows Karen's method.

   First I added 100 to 483, which gives me 583. But I added too much, so then I subtracted 10 from 583. The answer is $573.

   $$483 \xrightarrow{+100} 583 \xrightarrow{-10} 573$$

3. Rewrite the following problems as arrow strings and then solve them. Each arrow string should use Karen's method to make the calculation easier to do mentally.

   a.   56 + 28 =

   b.   327 + 51 =

   c.   956 + 98 =

1. a. 646

   b. 536

   c. 8,134

   d. 162

   e. 21,752

2. Sample student explanation:

For each problem, I added 100 and then subtracted 1 because 99 is one less than 100.

3. Sample responses:

   a. $56 \xrightarrow{\ +\ 30\ } 86 \xrightarrow{\ -\ 2\ } 84.$

First I added 30 to 56, which gives me 86. But I added too much, so then I subtracted 2 from 86. The answer is 84.

   b. $327 \xrightarrow{\ +\ 50\ } 377 \xrightarrow{\ +\ 1\ } 378.$

First I added 50 to 327, which gives me 377. I then added one extra, which gave me the answer of 378.

   c. $956 \xrightarrow{\ +\ 100\ } 1,056 \xrightarrow{\ -\ 2\ } 1,054.$

First I added 100 to 956, which gives me 1,056. But I added too much, so I subtracted 2 from 1,056. The answer is 1,054.

Two Steps for Efficiency (page 2)

When you choose an appropriate strategy, some subtraction problems become easy too. For example 465 − 37.

If I think 465 − 40. I subtracted three too many...

So I have to add three at the end to make up for taking away too many.

You can use arrow strings to show this strategy:

465 $\xrightarrow{-40}$ _____ $\xrightarrow{+3}$ _____

4. Fill in the blanks.

Solve the following subtraction problems mentally. Use arrow strings to show what strategy you used.

5. **a.**   743 − 92 =

   b.   132 − 85 =

   c.   578 − 99 =

   d.   1643 − 75 =

4. $465 \xrightarrow{-40} 425 \xrightarrow{+3} 428$

5. Sample strategies:

    a. $743 \xrightarrow{-100} 643 \xrightarrow{+8} 651$

    b. $132 \xrightarrow{-100} 32 \xrightarrow{+15} 47$

    c. $578 \xrightarrow{-100} 478 \xrightarrow{+1} 479$

    d. $1{,}643 \xrightarrow{-100} 1{,}543 \xrightarrow{+25} 1{,}568$

Make It Easy

1. Solve the following addition and subtraction problems mentally.
   Use arrow strings to show what strategy you used.

   a.   624 + 99 =

   b.   624 − 99 =

   c.   5,444 + 999 =

   d.   5,444 − 999 =

   e.   832 + 90 =

   f.   832 − 90 =

   g.   1,573 + 98 =

   h.   1,573 − 98 =

   i.   365 + 997 =

   j.   4,526 − 997 =

   k.   6,000 − 991 =

   l.   5,001 + 998 =

1. Sample strategies:

   a. 624 $\xrightarrow{\ +\ 100\ }$ 724 $\xrightarrow{\ -\ 1\ }$ 723

   b. 624 $\xrightarrow{\ -\ 100\ }$ 524 $\xrightarrow{\ +\ 1\ }$ 525

   c. 5,444 $\xrightarrow{\ +\ 1,000\ }$ 6,444 $\xrightarrow{\ -\ 1\ }$ 6,443

   d. 5,444 $\xrightarrow{\ -\ 1,000\ }$ 4,444 $\xrightarrow{\ +\ 1\ }$ 4,445

   e. 832 $\xrightarrow{\ +\ 100\ }$ 932 $\xrightarrow{\ -\ 10\ }$ 922

   f. 832 $\xrightarrow{\ -\ 100\ }$ 732 $\xrightarrow{\ +\ 10\ }$ 742

   g. 1,573 $\xrightarrow{\ +\ 100\ }$ 1,673 $\xrightarrow{\ -\ 2\ }$ 1,671

   h. 1,573 $\xrightarrow{\ -\ 100\ }$ 1,473 $\xrightarrow{\ +\ 2\ }$ 1,475

   i. 365 $\xrightarrow{\ +\ 1,000\ }$ 1,365 $\xrightarrow{\ -\ 3\ }$ 1,362

   j. 4,526 $\xrightarrow{\ -\ 1,000\ }$ 3,526 $\xrightarrow{\ +\ 3\ }$ 3,529

   k. 6,000 $\xrightarrow{\ -\ 1,000\ }$ 5,000 $\xrightarrow{\ +\ 9\ }$ 5,009

   l. 5,001 $\xrightarrow{\ +\ 1,000\ }$ 6,001 $\xrightarrow{\ -\ 2\ }$ 5,999

Recipes (page 1)

Banana Shake

4 servings:

2 bananas

$\frac{1}{3}$ cup lemon juice

$\frac{1}{4}$ cup granulated sugar

$\frac{1}{2}$ quart milk

1 cup vanilla ice cream

Blend until smooth.

Tanisha's favorite summertime drink is a banana shake.
She started the following chart so she would know how
to make the shake when different numbers of guests join
her. Help Tanisha by filling in her chart.

Servings	4	8		6			
Bananas	2		1		6		
Lemon Juice (cups)	$\frac{1}{3}$						$\frac{1}{12}$
Sugar (cups)	$\frac{1}{4}$						
Milk (quarts)	$\frac{1}{2}$					2	
Ice Cream (cups)	1		$\frac{1}{2}$		3		$\frac{1}{4}$

Servings	4	8	2	6	12	16	1
Bananas	2	4	1	3	6	8	$\frac{1}{2}$
Lemon Juice (cups)	$\frac{1}{3}$	$\frac{2}{3}$	$\frac{1}{6}$	$\frac{3}{6}$	1	$1\frac{1}{3}$	$\frac{1}{12}$
Sugar (cups)	$\frac{1}{4}$	$\frac{1}{2}$	$\frac{1}{8}$	$\frac{3}{8}$	$\frac{6}{8}$	1	$\frac{1}{16}$
Milk (quarts)	$\frac{1}{2}$	1	$\frac{1}{4}$	$\frac{3}{4}$	$1\frac{1}{2}$	2	$\frac{1}{8}$
Ice Cream (cups)	1	2	$\frac{1}{2}$	$1\frac{1}{2}$	3	4	$\frac{1}{4}$

Note: An important and useful skill for students to use is the idea of halving and doubling a fractional amount. It is important they can make sense of the following situations.

- How much is half of $\frac{1}{2}$ cup rice?
- How much is half of one half cup water?
- What is half of $\frac{1}{4}$ cup peanut butter?
- What is double $\frac{1}{8}$ cup water? What is double $\frac{1}{4}$ cup water?
- What do I get when I put together $\frac{1}{2}$ cup rice and $\frac{1}{4}$ cup rice?

The context provides a way for them to reason. You might have a class discussion about recipes beforehand using measuring cups and a fraction bar. You might want to provide students with rectangle strips of paper they use to reason with. Students can fold the strip to make fourths, and then take half by folding it once more. It helps to have a new strip for thirds, fifths, and so on. The strips do not have to be the same size unless they are combining fractional parts together.

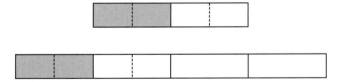

If students are having difficulty, you might suggest that they look at different column relationships. For example, if they have trouble combing 4 servings and 2 servings to make 6 servings, perhaps they can do the next column, where they need to combine 4 servings and 8 servings to make 12 servings.

Encourage students to check their work by asking:

- Are the ingredients for 6 servings exactly half the ingredients for 12 servings?
- Are the ingredients for 16 servings quadruple the amount for 4 servings?

Have students share strategies they used to fill in the chart.

Recipes (page 2)

Strawberry Punch

8 servings:

$\frac{2}{3}$ cup lemon juice

$\frac{1}{4}$ cup granulated sugar

$1\frac{1}{3}$ cups strawberries, sliced

4 cups ginger ale

16 ice cubes

Stir ingredients together in a punch bowl.

Alonzo likes to make punch for his friends on a hot summer day. He started the following chart so he will know how to make strawberry punch when guests join him. Help Alonzo by filling in the rest of his chart.

Servings	8	4	16		20			
Lemon Juice (cups)	$\frac{2}{3}$			2				
Sugar (cups)	$\frac{1}{4}$						$1\frac{1}{4}$	
Strawberries (cups)	$1\frac{1}{3}$					2		
Ginger Ale (cups)	4							18
Ice Cubes	16							

Servings	8	4	16	24	20	12	40	36
Lemon Juice (cups)	$\frac{2}{3}$	$\frac{1}{3}$	$1\frac{1}{3}$	2	$1\frac{2}{3}$	1	$3\frac{1}{3}$	3
Sugar (cups)	$\frac{1}{4}$	$\frac{1}{8}$	$\frac{1}{2}$	$\frac{3}{4}$	$\frac{5}{8}$	$\frac{3}{8}$	$1\frac{1}{4}$	$1\frac{1}{8}$
Strawberries (cups)	$1\frac{1}{3}$	$\frac{2}{3}$	$2\frac{2}{3}$	4	$3\frac{1}{3}$	2	$6\frac{2}{3}$	6
Ginger Ale (cups)	4	2	8	12	10	6	20	18
Ice Cubes	16	8	32	48	40	24	80	72

Notes: Here are some probes teachers have used to encourage students to reason on their own.

If students are having difficulty taking half of $1\frac{1}{3}$:

Draw a picture of what $1\frac{1}{3}$ looks like, using a fraction bar.

- How can you use your picture to take half of this amount?

How many $\frac{1}{4}$ cups sugar do you need to make $1\frac{1}{4}$ cups sugar?

- You need 5 quarter cups, so 8 servings × 5 is 40 servings

How can you get the number of servings to use 18 cups of ginger ale?

- For the 4-servings column, you need 2 cups ginger ale. To make 18 cups, you need nine times that amount, so 4 servings times 9 is 36 servings.

- For the 8-servings column, you need 4 cups. For 18 cups, 4c + 4c + 4c + 4c +2c, you need four times 8 servings and one 4 serving. This makes 36 servings.

What columns can you use to make 24 servings?

- Triple 8 servings
- Six times 4 servings.
- Combine 8 servings and 16 servings

What columns can you use to make 20 servings?

- 24 servings minus 4 servings
- Five times 4 servings

East of Yaksee Cave (page 1)

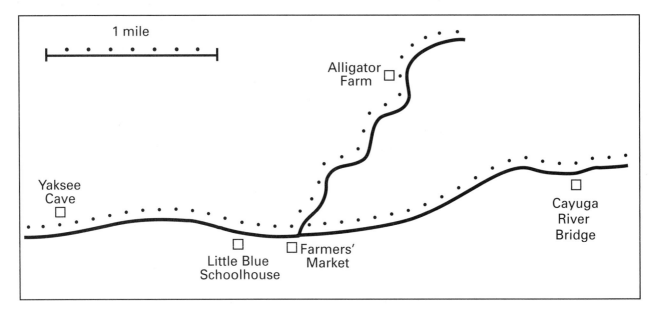

1. There is a scale line on the map. What information can you use from this scale line?

Here is a distance table for this map. Distances from the Little Blue Schoolhouse are along the first row. For example, it is $\frac{3}{8}$ of a mile from the Schoolhouse to the Farmers' Market.

	Little Blue Schoolhouse	Yaksee Cave	Farmers' Market	Alligator Farm	Cayuga River Bridge
Little Blue Schoolhouse	0	$1\frac{3}{8}$ mile	$\frac{3}{8}$ mile	$1\frac{6}{8}$ or $1\frac{3}{4}$ miles	$2\frac{1}{2}$ miles
Yaksee Cave					
Farmers' Market					
Alligator Farm					
Cayuga River Bridge					

2. Use the map to fill in the rest of the distance table. Whenever possible, express the fractional distances as halves or quarters instead of eighths of a mile.

1. The scale line tells you how one mile is divided in eight parts; each part is $\frac{1}{8}$ of a mile. This makes it possible to use the map to find the distance from Yaksee Cave to Little Blue Schoolhouse; 7 marks is $7 \times \frac{1}{8}$ or $\frac{7}{8}$ of a mile.

Note: Labeling the map scale helps students build upon the relationship between halves, quarters, and eighths of a mile.

1 mile

$\frac{1}{8}$	$\frac{2}{8}$	$\frac{3}{8}$	$\frac{4}{8}$	$\frac{5}{8}$	$\frac{6}{8}$	$\frac{7}{8}$	$\frac{8}{8}$
	$\frac{1}{4}$		$\frac{2}{4}$		$\frac{3}{4}$		$\frac{4}{4}$
			$\frac{1}{2}$				$\frac{2}{2}$
							1

2. Here is the distance table in miles.

Note: Encourage students to reduce their fractions—for example, reduce $\frac{4}{8}$ to $\frac{1}{2}$.

	Little Blue Schoolhouse	Yaksee Cave	Farmers' Market	Alligator Farm	Cayuga River Bridge
Little Blue Schoolhouse	0	$1\frac{3}{8}$ mile	$\frac{3}{8}$ mile	$1\frac{6}{8}$ or $1\frac{3}{4}$ miles	$2\frac{1}{2}$ miles
Yaksee Cave	$1\frac{3}{8}$	0	$1\frac{6}{8}$ or $1\frac{3}{4}$	$3\frac{1}{8}$	$3\frac{7}{8}$
Farmers' Market	$\frac{3}{8}$	$1\frac{6}{8}$ or $1\frac{3}{4}$	0	$1\frac{3}{8}$	$2\frac{1}{8}$
Alligator Farm	$1\frac{6}{8}$ or $1\frac{3}{4}$	$3\frac{1}{8}$	$1\frac{3}{8}$	0	$3\frac{1}{2}$
Cayuga River Bridge	$2\frac{1}{2}$	$3\frac{7}{8}$	$2\frac{1}{8}$	$3\frac{1}{2}$	0

East of Yaksee Cave (page 2)

A new sign will be placed at the intersection near the Farmers' Market.

This sign will have information about distances expressed in miles and in minutes walking. Expressing distance in time is helpful for visitors.

3. Use your previous work with Yaksee Cave to fill in the mile distances on the sign.

To calculate the distances in minutes walking, you can use a double scale line with miles and minutes. It takes about 60 minutes to walk 2 miles.

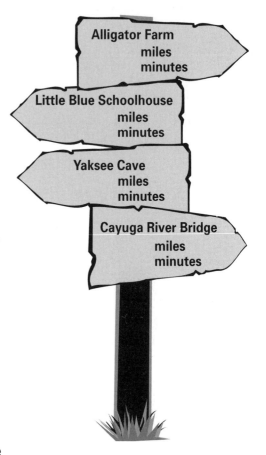

4. Use the double scale line to estimate the minute distances on the sign. Complete the sign.

3. Little Blue Schoolhouse $\frac{3}{8}$ miles

Yaksee Cave $1\frac{3}{4}$ miles

Alligator Farm $1\frac{3}{8}$ miles

Cayuga River Bridge $2\frac{1}{8}$ miles

4.

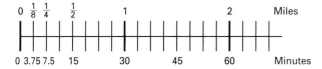

Little Blue Schoolhouse $\frac{3}{8}$ miles about 11 minutes (or 11.25 minutes)

Yaksee Cave $1\frac{3}{4}$ miles about 53 minutes (or 52.5 minutes)

Alligator Farm $1\frac{3}{8}$ miles about 41 minutes (or 41.25 minutes)

Cayuga River Bridge $2\frac{1}{8}$ miles about 64 minutes (or 63.75 minutes)

Passing by Tom's House

Here is a map of the area near Tom's house. This map does not show a scale line.

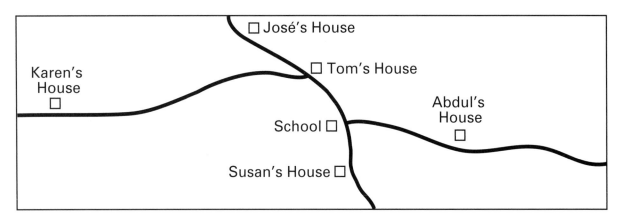

The distances on the map are to scale. To use this map, you can use the information in the first row of the distance table below. It shows the distance from the school to each person's home.

	School	Tom	José	Karen	Abdul	Susan
School	0	$\frac{3}{4}$ mi	$1\frac{1}{2}$ mi	3 mi	$1\frac{1}{8}$ mi	$\frac{5}{8}$ mi
Tom						
José						
Karen						
Abdul						
Susan						

1. Fill in the rest of the distance table. Whenever possible, express the distances as halves or quarters instead of eighths of a mile.

You can write a subtraction number sentence to represent distances. For example, the distance from Tom's house to José's is $1\frac{1}{2} - \frac{3}{4} = \frac{3}{4}$.

2. Use the distance information to write six number sentences using both addition and subtraction.

Passing by Tom's House

1. Answers below are given in miles.

	School	Tom	José	Karen	Abdul	Susan
School	0	$\frac{3}{4}$ mi	$1\frac{1}{2}$ mi	3 mi	$1\frac{1}{8}$ mi	$\frac{5}{8}$ mi
Tom	$\frac{3}{4}$	0	$\frac{3}{4}$	$2\frac{1}{4}$	$1\frac{7}{8}$	$1\frac{3}{8}$
José	$1\frac{1}{2}$	$\frac{3}{4}$	0	3	$2\frac{5}{8}$	$2\frac{1}{8}$
Karen	3	$2\frac{1}{4}$	3	0	$4\frac{1}{8}$	$3\frac{5}{8}$
Abdul	$1\frac{1}{8}$	$1\frac{7}{8}$	$2\frac{5}{8}$	$4\frac{1}{8}$	0	$1\frac{3}{4}$
Susan	$\frac{5}{8}$	$1\frac{3}{8}$	$2\frac{1}{8}$	$3\frac{5}{8}$	$1\frac{3}{4}$	0

2. Some possibilities:

Addition:

$1\frac{1}{8} + 1\frac{1}{2} = 2\frac{5}{8}$ $\frac{5}{8} + 1\frac{1}{2} = 2\frac{1}{8}$ $\frac{5}{8} + \frac{3}{4} = 1\frac{3}{8}$

Subtraction:

$3 - \frac{3}{4} = 2\frac{1}{4}$ $1\frac{1}{8} - \frac{5}{8} = \frac{1}{2}$ $1\frac{3}{4} - 1\frac{1}{2} = \frac{1}{4}$

Encourage students to simplify their answers by reducing fractions.

Notes: If students struggle with these problems, you may have them use a number line with fractions. To add or subtract is making jumps on the number line.

Finding the distance between Karen and Tom's house involves the subtraction of fractions: $3 - \frac{3}{4} = 2\frac{1}{4}$.

The same applies to the distance between José and Tom's house:

$1\frac{1}{2} - \frac{3}{4} = \frac{3}{4}$

Finding the other distances involves addition, for example, the distance between Abdul and Susan's house: $1\frac{1}{8} + \frac{5}{8} = 1\frac{6}{8}$ or $1\frac{3}{4}$

Extension

Have students relate their fraction equations from problem **2** to the map. For example, the problem $1\frac{1}{8} + 1\frac{1}{2} = 2\frac{5}{8}$ relates to the combination of the distances from Abdul's house to the school and from the school to José's house.

Driving to Mons

The town of Mons is close to five other cities.

This map shows the driving distance from Mons to each of the nearby cities. The distance is expressed in hours.

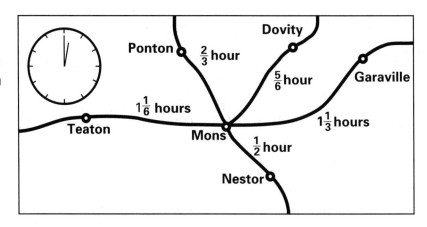

Here is a driving distance table for the cities near Mons. The map information is recorded in the table as hours and minutes. For example, the distance from Mons to Ponton is $\frac{2}{3}$ of an hour. In the table, it is recorded as 40 minutes.

	Mons	Ponton	Dovity	Garaville	Nestor	Teaton
Mons	0	40 min	50 min	1 hr 20 min	30 min	1 hr 10 min
Ponton						
Dovity						
Garaville						
Nestor						
Teaton						

1. Fill in the rest of the distance table.

2. To drive from Ponton to Dovity, you need $\frac{2}{3}$ hour + $\frac{5}{6}$ hour.
   a. What time did you enter in your table?
   b. Use your answer to problem **a** to explain that $\frac{2}{3} + \frac{5}{6} = 1\frac{1}{2}$.

3. a. How many hours and minutes is $\frac{1}{2}$ hr + $1\frac{1}{3}$ hrs?
   b. Use your answer to problem a. to explain that $\frac{1}{2} + 1\frac{1}{3} = 1\frac{5}{6}$.

4. Solve the following addition problems. It may be helpful to think of hours and minutes.

   a. $\frac{1}{3} + 1\frac{1}{6}$ b. $\frac{1}{2} + \frac{1}{6}$

Driving to Mons

Before starting with the problems on this page, you might want to show students how to divide the 12 markings on the face of a clock into halves, thirds, and sixths to help them better understand how to work with these fractions.

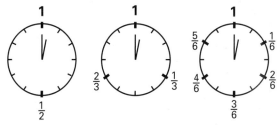

Students can then refer to these clocks for help with adding fractions. For example, a clock could be used to add $\frac{1}{2}$ hour + $\frac{1}{3}$ hour as shown below:

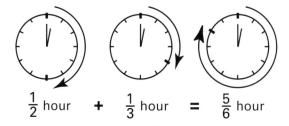

$$\frac{1}{2} \text{ hour} \quad + \quad \frac{1}{3} \text{ hour} \quad = \quad \frac{5}{6} \text{ hour}$$

A half hour is six markings, and a third of an hour is four markings, for a total of 10 markings, or $\frac{5}{6}$ of an hour.

Since an hour is equal to 60 minutes, $\frac{1}{6}$ of an hour is equal to 10 minutes. $\frac{1}{3}$ of an hour is equal to 20 minutes. Some students may need to write some of these relationships before starting to fill in the table.

2. a. 1 hr 30 min

b. From Ponton to Dovity is $\frac{2}{3} + \frac{5}{6}$ hours. My total time was 1 hour and 30 minutes, which is equivalent to $1\frac{1}{2}$ hours.

3. a. $\frac{1}{2}$ hr + $1\frac{1}{3}$ hr = 30 min + 1 hour + 20 min = 1 hour and 50 minutes.

b. 1 hour and 50 minutes is equivalent to $1\frac{5}{6}$ hours, since 10 minutes is equal to $\frac{1}{6}$ of an hour and 50 minutes is equal to $5 \times \frac{1}{6} = \frac{5}{6}$ of an hour.

4. a. $\frac{1}{3} + 1\frac{1}{6} = 1\frac{1}{2}$ **b.** $\frac{1}{2} + \frac{1}{6} = \frac{2}{3}$

1.

	Mons	Ponton	Dovity	Garaville	Nestor	Teaton
Mons	0	40 min	50 min	1 hr 20 min	30 min	1 hr 10 min
Ponton	40 min	0	1 hr 30 min	2 hr	1 hr 10 min	1 hr 50 min
Dovity	50 min	1 hr 30 min	0	2 hr 10 min	1 hr 20 min	2 hr
Garaville	1 hr 20 min	2 hr	2 hr 10 min	0	1 hr 50 min	2 hr 30 min
Nestor	30 min	1 hr 10 min	1 hr 20 min	1 hr 50 min	0	1 hr 40 min
Teaton	1 hr 10 min	1 hr 50 min	2 hr	2 hr 30 min	1 hr 40 min	0

Sisters (page 1)

Ms. Nakamura's students take a survey and discover that $\frac{1}{2}$ of the students in the class have only one sister and $\frac{1}{3}$ have more than one sister. The class displays the survey results in the pie chart.

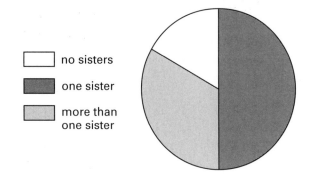

1. **a.** What fraction of the class has no sisters?

   b. What fraction of the class has one or more sisters?

   c. Can it be possible that there were 20 students involved in the survey? Explain why or why not.

Mr. Brown's class conducted the same survey. Twenty-four students were involved in this survey. Six students had only one sister, and four students had more than one sister.

To display the survey results, you can make a pie chart, but you also can use a segmented bar.

On this bar with twenty-four segments, each segment represents one student.

2. **a.** Use colors to display the survey results for Mr. Brown's class.

   b. What fraction of the class has one sister or more?

   c. What fraction of the class has no sister? Explain your answer.

3. Is it possible to display the survey results of this survey on a bar with only twelve segments? Explain why or why not.

1. a. $\frac{1}{6}$ of the class has no sisters. Sample explanations:

- Add extra lines in the pie chart as shown below to show that the white part is $\frac{1}{6}$ of the whole pie chart.

- Find the fraction you have to add to $\frac{1}{2}$ and $\frac{1}{3}$ and get a whole number.

$$\frac{1}{2} + \frac{1}{3} =$$
$$\frac{3}{6} + \frac{2}{6} = \frac{5}{6} \text{ and } 1 - \frac{5}{6} = \frac{1}{6}$$

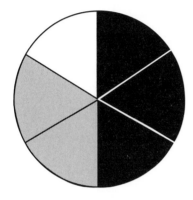

b. $\frac{5}{6}$ of the class has one or more sisters. Sample explanation:

- Use the pie chart with the extra lines to show that $\frac{5}{6}$ of the pie chart is other than white.

c. It is not possible that 20 students were involved in the survey, because 20 is not divisible by 6 or by 3.

2. a.

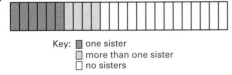

Key: ■ one sister
　　 ▨ more than one sister
　　 □ no sisters

b. 10 out of 24 or $\frac{10}{24}$ or $\frac{5}{12}$ of Mr. Brown's class has one or more sisters.

c. 14 out of 24 or $\frac{14}{24}$ or $\frac{7}{12}$ of Mr. Brown's class has no sister.

3. Yes, it is possible to display the survey results in a bar with twelve segments.

Possible explanations:

- Instead of 24 segments, the new bar has 12 segments, which is one half. You can take half of all the previous segments: $\frac{1}{2} \times 6 = 3$; $\frac{1}{2} \times 4 = 2$, and $\frac{1}{2} \times 14 = 7$

Each segment represents 2 students.

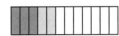

Sisters (page 2)

If you want to add fractions with different denominators, you can make bars, each with the same number of segments, to represent the fractions. For example, $\frac{1}{4} + \frac{1}{6}$ can be solved by using two bars with 12 segments each.

$\frac{1}{4}$ of 12 segments is three segments.

$\frac{1}{6}$ of 12 segments is two segments.

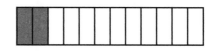

The total is five out of twelve segments:

$$\frac{1}{4} + \frac{1}{6} = \frac{3}{12} + \frac{2}{12}$$
$$= \frac{5}{12}$$

4. Explain why you could also use two bars with 24 segments each to add $\frac{1}{4}$ and $\frac{1}{6}$.

5. Solve the following addition problems. If necessary, make two bars, each with the same number of segments, to represent the two fractions.

a. $\frac{1}{4} + \frac{1}{8} =$ f. $\frac{3}{8} + \frac{1}{2} =$

b. $\frac{2}{3} + \frac{1}{4} =$ g. $\frac{1}{3} + \frac{1}{5} =$

c. $\frac{1}{2} + \frac{1}{6} =$ h. $\frac{2}{6} + \frac{1}{4} =$

d. $\frac{1}{6} + \frac{4}{9} =$ i. $\frac{2}{4} + \frac{3}{10} =$

e. $\frac{1}{10} + \frac{3}{4} =$

4. Sample explanation:

If the bar has 24 segments, it is easy to shade $\frac{1}{4}$ of the segments; it would be 6 segments and $\frac{1}{6}$ of the segments is 4 segments. It works well because 24 is divisible by both 4 and 6.

5.

a. $\frac{1}{4} + \frac{1}{8} = \frac{3}{8}$ **b.** $\frac{2}{3} + \frac{1}{4} = \frac{11}{12}$ **c.** $\frac{1}{2} + \frac{1}{6} = \frac{4}{6}$ or $\frac{2}{3}$

   $\frac{1}{4} = \frac{2}{8}$ $\frac{2}{3} = \frac{8}{12}$ $\frac{1}{2} = \frac{3}{6}$

   $\frac{1}{8}$ $\frac{1}{4} = \frac{3}{12}$ $\frac{1}{6}$

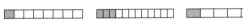

d. $\frac{1}{6} + \frac{4}{9} = \frac{11}{18}$ **e.** $\frac{1}{10} + \frac{3}{4} = \frac{17}{20}$ **f.** $\frac{3}{8} + \frac{1}{2} = \frac{7}{8}$

   $\frac{1}{6} = \frac{3}{18}$ $\frac{1}{10} = \frac{2}{20}$ $\frac{3}{8}$

   $\frac{4}{9} = \frac{8}{18}$ $\frac{3}{4} = \frac{15}{20}$ $\frac{1}{2} = \frac{4}{8}$

g. $\frac{1}{3} + \frac{1}{5} = \frac{8}{15}$ **h.** $\frac{2}{6} + \frac{1}{4} = \frac{7}{12}$ **i.** $\frac{2}{4} + \frac{3}{10} = \frac{8}{10}$ or $\frac{4}{5}$

   $\frac{1}{3} = \frac{5}{15}$ $\frac{2}{6} = \frac{4}{12}$ $\frac{2}{4} = \frac{1}{2}$ and $\frac{1}{2} = \frac{5}{10}$

   $\frac{1}{5} = \frac{3}{15}$ $\frac{1}{4} = \frac{3}{12}$ $\frac{3}{10}$

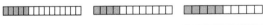

School Plays

The high school Drama Club produced seven plays last year in different places around town. Some of the plays were more popular than other plays. The club kept track of attendance using the percent bars.

For each play, fill in the information to express the attendance as a fraction, as a percent, and as the number of seats occupied.

1.

Fraction occupied: _____

Percent occupied: _____

Seats occupied: _____

2.

Fraction occupied: _____

Percent occupied: _____

Seats occupied: _____

3.

Fraction occupied: _____

Percent occupied: _____

Seats occupied: _____

4.

Fraction occupied: _____

Percent occupied: _____

Seats occupied: _____

5.

Fraction occupied: _____

Percent occupied: _____

Seats occupied: _____

6.

Fraction occupied: _____

Percent occupied: _____

Seats occupied: _____

7.

Fraction occupied: _____

Percent occupied: _____

Seats occupied: _____

1. Fraction occupied: $\frac{1}{4}$

   Percent occupied: 25%
   Seats occupied: 100

2. Fraction occupied: $\frac{1}{2}$

   Percent occupied: 50%
   Seats occupied: 250

3. Fraction occupied: $\frac{1}{3}$

   Percent occupied: 33%
   Seats occupied: 30

4. Fraction occupied: $\frac{1}{5}$

   Percent occupied: 20%
   Seats occupied: 40

5. Fraction occupied: $\frac{2}{3}$

   Percent occupied: 67%
   Seats occupied: 80

6. Fraction occupied: $\frac{3}{4}$

   Percent occupied: 75%
   Seats occupied: 90

7. Fraction occupied: $\frac{3}{5}$

   Percent occupied: 60%
   Seats occupied: 210

Per 100 (page 1)

There is a great rivalry between the sports teams of East Middle School and West Middle School.

1. At the last basketball game between East and West, there were 160 East fans and 240 West fans. The sports writer for the East Middle School newspaper wanted to report the percentages of fans for each school.

    a. Fill in this ratio table to account for a total of 100 spectators.

East Fans	160				
West Fans	240				
Total Fans	400				

    b. What percent of the fans at the basketball game were East fans? And the percentage of West fans?

    c. What was the ratio of East fans to West fans? Write this ratio in simplest form using the smallest whole numbers but keeping the ratio intact.

2. At the last gymnastics meet between the two schools, the ratio of East fans to West fans was 13 to 7.

    a. What percent of the fans at the gymnastic meet were East fans? And the percentage of West fans?

East Fans					
West Fans					
Total Fans					

    b. Shade and label the following percent bars to show the percentages of East fans and West fans.

    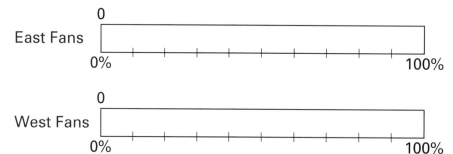

    c. There were 180 fans at the gymnastics meet. Use either a percent bar or a ratio table to find the number of fans for each team.

1. a. Sample table:

East Fans	160	80	40		
West Fans	240	120	60		
Total Fans	400	200	100		

- Using a ratio table.

East Fans	65	13	26	52	117
West Fans	35	7	14	28	63
Total Fans	100	20	40	80	180

b. For every 100 fans, there are 40 East fans and 60 West fans, so of the fans attending the game, 40% were East fans, and 60% were West fans.

c. The ratio of East fans to West fans is 40:60 or, written with the smallest whole numbers, 2:3.

2. a. For every 100 fans, there are 65 East fans and 35 West fans, so of the fans attending the meet, 65% were East fans and 35% were West fans.

East Fans	13	65			
West Fans	7	35			
Total Fans	20	100			

b.

East Fans
0
0%   65%   100%

West Fans
0
0%   35%   100%

c. There are 117 East fans and 63 West fans. Sample solutions:

- $90 + 18 + 9 = 117$ East fans. The leftover is $180 - 117$ or 63 West fans.

- Using a percent bar:

East Fans
0 9 18   90   180
0% 10%   65%   100%
    5%   50%

3. At the last swim meet between the two schools, there were only 280 East fans and 220 West fans.

   What percent of the fans at the swim meet were East fans? And the percentage of West fans? Show your strategy.

4. **a.** At which of the sporting events mentioned in problems 1–3 did East Middle School have the highest percentage of fans?

   b. At which sporting event did East Middle School have the most fans?

3. 56% East fans; 44% West fans. Sample strategy, using a ratio table:

East Fans	280	28	56
West Fans	220	22	44
Total Fans	500	50	100

4. a. At the gymnastics meet.

Basketball game:	40%
Gymnastics meet:	65%
Swim meet:	56%

b. At the swim meet.

Basketball game:	160
Gymnastics meet:	117
Swim meet:	280

From Ratios to Percents (page 1)

Here are two methods you can use to convert a ratio into a percent.

- The Ratio Method: Use a ratio table to calculate how many per 100.

- The Fraction Method: Rewrite the ratio as a fraction and then use the relationship between fractions, decimals, and percents.

1. Two out of five students have read *The Hobbit*. Use each of the methods described above to find a percent equivalent to the ratio two out of five.

Ratio Table Method:

Part						
Whole						

Fraction Method:

2. Two out of three students have read *The Diary of Anne Frank*. Use each of the methods described above to find a percent equivalent to the ratio two out of three.

Ratio Table Method:

Part						
Whole						

Fraction Method:

1. 40%

Strategy 1—Using the Fraction Method:

Two out of five is the same as $\frac{2}{5}$.
Since $\frac{1}{5}$ equals 20%, $\frac{2}{5}$ equals 40%.

Strategy 2—Using the Ratio Method:

		× 2	× 10	
Part that read *The Hobbit*	2	4	40
Whole	5	10	100

Some students may already be familiar with a third
strategy—Using the Decimal Method:

Two out of 5 is $2 \div 5$ or 0.4 and 0.4 = 0.40. This is the
same as $\frac{40}{100}$, or 40 out of 100, thus 40%.

2. $66\frac{2}{3}$% or 67%

Strategy 1—Using the Fraction Method:

Two out of three is the same as $\frac{2}{3}$; $\frac{1}{3}$ equals
$33\frac{1}{3}$%, so $\frac{2}{3}$ equals $66\frac{2}{3}$%.

Strategy 2—Using the Ratio Method:

Part that read *The Diary...*	2	$\frac{2}{3}$	6	66	$66\frac{2}{3}$
Whole	3	1	9	99	100

Strategy 3—Using the Decimal Method:

$2 \div 3 = 0.66666667 \approx 0.67$ which is the same as $\frac{67}{100}$,
or 67 out of 100, thus 67%

3. Find an equivalent percent for each of the following. Use any method, but show your work.

   a. Three out of 20 students participate in the Drama Club.

   b. Seven out of 10 students have a bicycle.

   c. Three out of four students have read *A Wrinkle in Time*.

   d. Three out of eight students have read *The Outsiders*.

   e. One out of three students has read *Roll of Thunder, Hear My Cry*.

   f. Eight out of 12 students have seen the movie *Jurassic Park*.

   g. Only one out of 12 students has read the book on which the movie *Jurassic Park* was based.

   h. The school has 250 students, but five are not in school today.

   i. Mrs. Robinson's class has 14 girls and 11 boys.

3. Accept answers rounded to the nearest percent.

a. 15%.

Strategy 1—Using the Ratio Method:

Part Participating...	3	6	9	15
Whole	20	40	60	100

Strategy 2—Using the Fraction Method:

Three out of 20 is the same as $\frac{3}{20}$; $\frac{1}{20}$ is 5%, so $\frac{3}{20}$ is 3 × 5%, which is 15%.

Some students may already be familiar with a third strategy—Using the Decimal Method:

Three out of 20 is the same as 3 ÷ 20 = 0.15. This is the same as $\frac{15}{100}$, or 15 out of 100, thus 15%.

b. 70%   **c.** 75%

d. 37.5 or 38%   **e.** $33\frac{1}{3}$% or 33%

f. $66\frac{2}{3}$% or 67%   **g.** $8\frac{1}{3}$% or 8%

h. 2%

i. 56% girls, 44% boys. Sample strategies:

Strategy 1—Using the Fraction Method:

If there are 14 girls and 11 boys, then there are a total of 25 students in the class. Fourteen out of 25 is the same as $\frac{14}{25}$, which equals 56%. The percent of boys is what is leftover:

100% − 56% = 44%.

Strategy 2—Using the Ratio Method:

Part – Girls	14	28	56
Whole – Class	25	50	100

Part – Boys	11	22	44
Whole – Class	25	50	100

Strategy 3—Using the Decimal Method:

14 ÷ 25 = 0.56 which is the same as $\frac{56}{100}$, or 56 out of 100, thus 56%.

11 ÷ 25 = 0.44 which is the same as $\frac{44}{100}$, or 44 out of 100, thus 44%.

Tipping

1. Ms. Eng usually gives a 10% tip in restaurants. Mr. Lonetree usually gives a 15% tip. Fill in the tip table below, to show what Ms. Eng and Mr. Lonetree would leave for a tip.

Restaurant	Bill	10% Tip	15% Tip
Hamburger Heaven	$13.65		
The Apple Dumplin' Diner	$ 7.42		
Frank's Pizza Palace	$29.10		
The Newton Grill	$52.85		
Chez Louis	$77.50		

2. Decide whether Ms. Eng or Mr. Lonetree left the given tip for each of the following bills. Explain your choice.

Total Bill   **Tip**

a. $32.08

b. $27.27

c. $ 8.32

d. $14.00

e. $19.58

Mathematics in Context

1. The answers given below are rounded to the nearest nickel.
   Accept answers that are reasonably close to these.

Restaurant	Bill	10% Tip	15% Tip
Hamburger Heaven	$13.65	$1.35	$2.05
The Apple Dumplin' Diner	$ 7.42	$ 0.75	$ 1.10
Frank's Pizza Palace	$29.10	$2.90	$4.35
The Newton Grill	$52.85	$5.30	$7.95
Chez Louis	$77.50	$7.75	$11.65

2. **a.** Mr. Lonetree left this tip. It is closer to 15% of the total bill.
   b. Ms. Eng left this tip. It is closer to 10% of the total bill.
   c. Ms. Eng left this tip. It is closer to 10% of the total bill.
   d. Mr. Lonetree left this tip. It is closer to 15% of the total bill.
   e. Mr. Lonetree left this tip. It is closer to 15% of the total bill.

Map It Out!

What comes to mind when you see $\frac{1}{4}$? Make a mental map of the many different meanings for $\frac{1}{4}$ by filling in the boxes around $\frac{1}{4}$. You may draw additional boxes if you need them. After you finish, work with a partner to make a poster for the mental map of $\frac{1}{4}$.

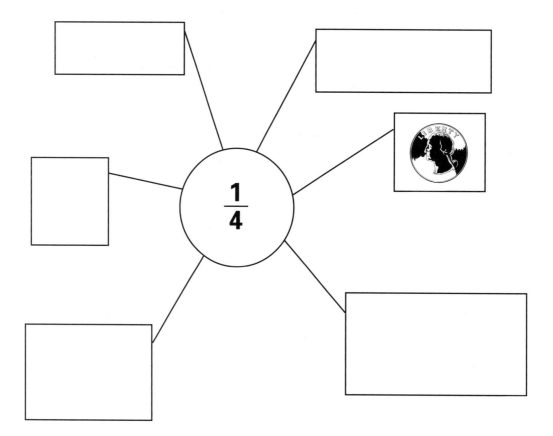

1. Have students exchange their facts. Many
different answers are possible. Some
examples of $\frac{1}{4}$:

Drawing of one quarter of an apple.

Quarter finals.

Quarter pound of cheese.

First quarter of the year.

First quarter of the cycle of the Moon.

25% off!

Number Sentences

Sandra, Barbara, and Vito create number sentences. They choose a target number and create number sentences using the four operations + − × ÷ and any of these numbers: **100 25 10 5 1**.

They decide to use the numbers only once, but it is not necessary to use all of the numbers.

They decide to use ( ), but not a calculator.

Here is their work for a target number of 750.

(100 − 25) × 10 = 750
Sandra

(10 × 5 + 25) × 100 = 750
Barbara

5 × 100 + 10 × 25 = 750
Vito

1. Who has a correct number sentence?

2. Create three different number sentences for each target.

    a.   Target is 1,500.

    b.   Target is 300.

    c.   Target is 535.

1. Sandra and Vito have correct number sentences.

Sandra has a correct number sentence.
$$(100 - 25) \times 10 =$$
$$75 \times 10 = 750$$

Barbara has an incorrect number sentence.
$$(10 \times 5 + 25) \times 100 =$$
$$(50 + 25) \times 100 =$$
$$75 \times 100 = 7{,}500$$

Note: Ask students how to make it correct.

Vito's number sentence is also correct.
$$5 \times 100 + 10 \times 25 =$$
$$500 + 250 = 750$$

2. Have students check each other's solutions. Here are some sample answers:

Game 1 $(25 - 10) \times 100 = 1{,}500$
$(10 + 5) \times 100 = 1{,}500$

Game 2 $(25 + 5) \times 10 = 300$
$[(10 \div 5) + 1] \times 100 = 300$

Game 3 $(100 \times 5) + (25 + 10) = 535$
$5 \times 100 + 25 + 10 = 535$

Extension

Have students try to find as many solutions as possible.

Too High, Too Low

Too High, Too Low

This is a game for two players.

- Player 1 secretly writes a decimal number between 0 and 10. The decimal number should be written only with tenths (one decimal place). Keep this number out of the other player's sight!

- Player 2 tries to guess the number.

- Player 1 responds that the guess is "Too high" or "Too low."

- Play continues until Player 2 guesses the number. Player 1 should keep a record of the number of guesses needed!

- Change roles and play again. The player who uses the least number of guesses wins the game.

Variations on this game:

- Choose a decimal number between 0 and –10. (Think of temperatures on a thermometer.)

- Choose a decimal number between 0 and 10, but the decimal number can be written containing hundredths (two decimal places).

Here is a recap of one game.

Player 1 chose 6.7

Player 2 guesses: Is it 5.7?

Player 1:   Too low

Player 2:   Is it 6.0?

Player 1:   Too low

Player 2:   Is it 7.0?

Player 1:   Too high

Player 2:   Is it 6.5?

Player 1:   Too low

Player 2:   Is it 6.8?

Player 1:   Too high

Player 2:   Is it 6.7?

Player 1: You got it in six guesses.

Certificates (page 1)

Climbers who reach the top of Mt. Erghoog earn a certificate.

The park station keeps many certificates on hand because Mt. Erghoog is a very popular mountain to climb.

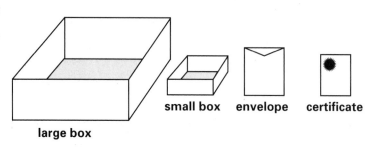

small box   envelope   certificate

large box

Certificates are shipped to the park station in large boxes.

Each large box contains 10 small boxes.

Inside each small box are 10 envelopes.

Inside each envelope are 10 certificates.

Raúl regularly takes inventory of the certificates to make sure they do not run out!

On May 1, here is what Raúl sees on the shelf. There are three loose certificates on the bottom shelf, and all the boxes and envelopes are full.

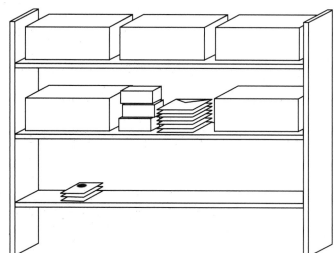

1. Help Raúl record the inventory by filling in this table.

Date	Large Boxes	Small Boxes	Envelopes	Certificates
May 1				

2. How many certificates were in stock on May 1?

1.

Date	Large Boxes	Small Boxes	Envelopes	Certificates
May 1	5	3	7	3

2. 5,373 certificates. Sample strategy:

I decided to unpack all the certificates.

Five large boxes contain 50 small boxes, which then gives a total of 53 small boxes. Fifty-three small boxes contain 530 envelopes, which then gives a total of 537 envelopes; 537 envelopes contain 5,370 certificates, and there are 3 loose certificates, which then gives a total of 5,373 certificates.

Note: Students should notice a correlation between the chart for problem 1 and the answer to problem 2. They should also realize at this point that there are 1,000 certificates in a large box and 100 certificates in a small box.

$5 \times 1,000 + 3 \times 100 + 7 \times 10 + 3 = 5,373$

Certificates (page 2)

3. Raúl took the inventory again on July 1. There were 29 large boxes, 16 small boxes, 8 envelopes, and 29 loose certificates. According to the computer, there should have been 30,709 certificates in stock. Was the actual number of certificates in agreement with the computer? Explain.

4. After one busy weekend, the shelf was in disarray. The workers opened too many boxes and envelopes unnecessarily. Here is what was on the shelf.

Large Boxes	Small Boxes	Envelopes	Certificates
21	19	48	38

Put the shelf back in order so that it would be easy to take inventory.

Large Boxes	Small Boxes	Envelopes	Certificates

5. On September 1, there are 2,015 certificates on the shelf. Fill in the table to show different ways the shelf might be organized.

Large Boxes	Small Boxes	Envelopes	Certificates

Mathematics in Context

3. Yes, the actual number of certificates was in agreement with the books. Sample explanation:

There were:

29,000 certificates in the 29 large boxes,

1,600 certificates in the 16 small boxes,

80 certificates in the 8 envelopes, and

29 loose certificates.

Adding these numbers gives a sum of 30,709. This sum is the same as the number in the books.

Note: Students might not understand how the computer is used to keep track of the certificates. Explain that the park station probably keeps track of each certificate handed out, and at various points in time, they enter this information into the computer. To find the remaining inventory amount without having to count, you can find the difference between the number of certificates handed out and the previous inventory amount.

4.

Large Boxes	Small Boxes	Envelopes	Certificates
21	19	48	38

You can organize the shelf like this:

Large Boxes	Small Boxes	Envelopes	Certificates
23	4	1	8

Two sample strategies:

Strategy One:

Find the total number of certificates by adding 21,000 + 1,900 + 480 + 38 = 23,418. Then split the total into its place values of 23, 4, 1, and 8.

Strategy Two:

Start at the right and "regroup" working to the left: 38 certificates equals certificates plus 3 envelopes that are grouped with the 48 resulting in 51 envelopes. 51 envelopes equal 1 envelope plus 5 small boxes which are grouped with the 19 resulting in 24, etc.

5. Answers will vary. Below are some possibilities.

Large Boxes	Small Boxes	Envelopes	Certificates
2	0	1	5
0	10	100	15
1	5	45	65
2	0	0	15
0	20	1	5
1	8	21	5

Note: In order to find many solutions to this problem, students must understand the relationships between large boxes, small boxes, envelopes, and certificates. For example, 20 small boxes hold as much as 2 large boxes.

Close Enough

Draw a circle around the number closest to the correct answer.
Do not use your calculator or make precise calculations. Write a
short explanation of how you made your selection.

1. 101 × 11 =

800

900

1,000

1,100

1,200

2. 391 × 391 =

10

100

1,000

10,000

100,000

1,000,000

3. 111 × 909 =

800

9,000

10,000

110,000

1,200,000

4. 91 × 19 × 19 =

500

5,000

50,000

500,000

5,000,000

5. 30 × 41 × 52 =

100

1,000

10,000

100,000

1,000,000

6. 1,234 × 5,678 =

1,000

10,000

100,000

1,000,000

10,000,000

1.–6. One sample estimation strategy is provided for each problem.

1. $101 \times 11 \approx 1,100$

I rounded to 101 to 100. $100 \times 11 = 1,100$. This shows that the answer is closest to 1,100.

Note: If students round the number 11 to 10, they will get $101 \times 10 = 1,010$, which is closest to 1,000. The problem here is that by rounding the 11 down to a 10, the answer is too low by 101 ($101 \times 11 = 101 \times 10 + 101$). This is a substantial difference. Point out to students that rounding the smaller number makes more of a difference than rounding the larger number. Probe: How far off is 1,100?

(11 too low; $101 \times 11 = 100 \times 11 + 1 \times 11$)

Students will probably find problem 1 to be the most challenging because the answer choices are the closest together.

2. $391 \times 391 \approx 100,000$

I rounded 391 to 400; so $400 \times 400 = 160,000$. This answer is closer to 100,000 than to 1,000,000.

3. $111 \times 909 \approx 110,000$

I rounded 909 to 1,000; so $111 \times 1,000 = 111,000$. This answer is closest to 110,000.

4. $91 \times 19 \times 19 \approx 50,000$

I rounded 91 to 100 and 19 to 20; so $100 \times 20 \times 20 = 40,000$. This answer is closest to 50,000.

5. $30 \times 41 \times 52 \approx 100,000$

I rounded 41 to 40 and 52 to 50; so $30 \times 40 \times 50 = 60,000$. Because I rounded down for the factors, the answer will be larger than 60,000. Therefore, the answer is closest to 100,000.

6. $1,234 \times 5,678 \approx 10,000,000$

I rounded to 1, 234 down to 1,000 and 5,678 down to 5,500;

$1,000 \times 5,500 = 5,500,000$.

Because I rounded down for each factor, the answer will be larger than 5,500,000. Therefore, the answer is closest to 10,000,000.

Rearrangements

How much money is 12 quarters? Study the pictures and you will find an easy solution.

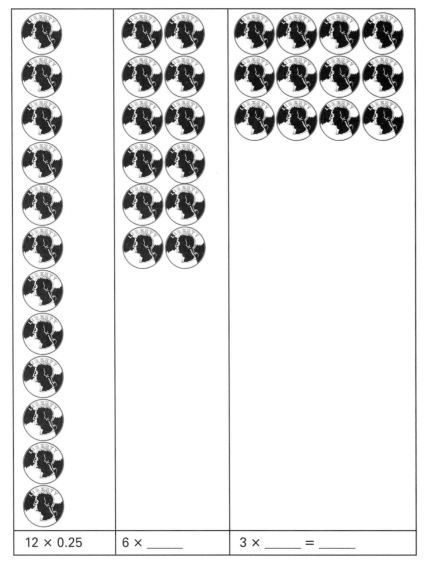

| 12 × 0.25 | 6 × _____ | 3 × _____ = _____ |

1. Fill in the blanks of the bottom row, to reflect each arrangement. Use the picture to explain this strategy.

2. Use a similar strategy to calculate the following problems mentally. Show your thinking.

   a. 8 × $0.25   **c.** 22 × $1.5

   b. 12 × $0.75   **d.** 16 × $1.25

1. $12 \times \$0.25 = 0.25 + 0.25 + 0.25 + 0.25 + 0.25$
$+ 0.25 + 0.25 + 0.25 + 0.25 + 0.25 + 0.25$
$+ 0.25$

If you want to find the value of 12 quarters, you can add $0.25 twelve times.

$6 \times \mathbf{\$0.50} = 12 \times 0.25$

Two quarters are the same value as $0.50. There are 6 groups of 2 quarters.

$3 \times \mathbf{\$1.00} = 3$

Four quarters equal $1. There are three groups of four quarters.

12×0.25 is the same as 6×0.50 which is the same as 3×1

If you double one of the factors, you need to take half of the other factor.

2. a. $8 \times \$0.25 =$
$\quad 4 \times \$0.50 =$
$\quad 2 \times \$1 = \$2$

b. $12 \times \$0.75 =$
$\quad 6 \times \$1.50 =$
$\quad 3 \times \$3 = \$9$

c. $22 \times \$1.5 =$
$\quad 11 \times \$3 = \$33$

d. $16 \times \$1.25 =$
$\quad 8 \times \$2.50 =$
$\quad 4 \times \$5 = \$20$

Lumber

Chucky's Lumber sells five different lengths of wood; 120 cm, 160 cm, 200 cm, 240 cm, and 280 cm.

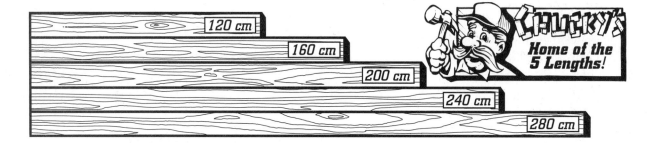

Here are some projects. Find the shortest piece of wood each person needs. Write your answers in the table.

	Lumber Sizes (in cm)				
	120	160	200	240	280
1.					
2.					
3.					
4.					
5.					
6.					
7.					
8.					
9.					
10.					

1. Peter is making a bookcase; he needs eight pieces of wood, each 34 cm long.
2. Teresa needs five pieces of wood, each 39 cm long.
3. Hua needs four pieces of wood, each 68 cm long.
4. Bobby needs three pieces of wood, each 82 cm long.
5. Mika needs six pieces of wood, each 41 cm long.
6. Avi needs four pieces of wood, each 63 cm long.
7. Margaret needs six pieces of wood, each 38 cm long.
8. Dieter needs five pieces of wood, each 47 cm long.
9. Uma needs 12 pieces of wood, each 21 cm long.
10. Jennifer needs nine pieces of wood, each 28 cm long.

Note: Since the lumberyard sells pieces of wood only in specific lengths, students do not need to know the exact length of wood needed for each problem. Students should be estimating the total length needed and then comparing their estimates to the lengths sold.

1. 280 centimeters (cm). Because 8 × 34 is more than 240
(8 × 30), Peter needs a piece longer than 240 cm.

2. 200 cm. Since 5 × 39 is less than 5 × 40,
a 200-cm piece is long enough for Teresa.

3. 280 cm. Since 4 × 68 is less than 4 × 70,
a 280-cm piece is long enough for Hua.

4. 280 cm. Since 3 × 82 is more than 240
(3 × 80), Bobby needs a piece longer than 240 cm.

5. 280 cm. Since 6 × 41 is more than 240
(6 × 40), Mika needs a piece longer than 240 cm.

6. 280 cm. Since 4 × 63 is more than 240
(4 × 60), Avi needs a 280-cm length.

7. 240 cm. Since 6 × 38 is less than 240
(6 × 40), Margaret needs a 240-cm length.

8. 240 cm. Since 5 × 47 = 235, which is less
than 240, Dieter needs a 240-cm length.

9. 280 cm. Since 12 × 21 is more than 240
(12 × 20), Uma needs a 280-cm length.

10. 280 cm. Since 9 × 28 is almost equal to 270
(9 × 30), which is more than 240, Jennifer
needs a 280-cm length.

Extension 1

Have students redo these problems, but tell them that the lumberyard ran out of pieces of wood 280 cm long, and each person wants to buy the fewest pieces of wood possible.

Extension 2

Have students redo these problems, but tell them that the number of pieces each person buys does not matter, and that they should find several possible combinations of lengths for each problem.

	Lumber Sizes (in cm)				
	120	160	200	240	280
1.					❙
2.			❙		
3.					❙
4.					❙
5.					❙
6.					❙
7.				❙	
8.				❙	
9.					❙
10.					❙

Estimations

Solve these problems without the use of a calculator.

1. Jacqueline earns $4.75 each time she washes her mother's car. How many times does she have to wash the car to save enough money to buy an MP3 player priced at $49?

2. On a shopping trip for his parents, Darnell purchased items worth $4.32, $3.76, $2.58, and $3.84. Estimate the total cost of the four items.

3. A can of baked beans costs $1.49. How many cans could you purchase with $10?

4. At a supermarket checkout, a woman has three items in her cart worth $3.75, $6.92, and $3.83. She realizes that she has only one $10 bill and one $5 bill. Does she have enough money to pay for the items?

5. Dieter needs pieces of lumber in the following lengths:
2 × 49 cm; 5 × 38 cm; 3 × 21 cm; 1 × 35 cm.

The lumber is sold in 1-meter lengths. How many 1-meter lengths will Dieter purchase?

6. Natasha works at a computer help desk. She makes notes of the time she spends with each customer.

A: 14 minutes	E: 38 minutes
B: 7 minutes	F: 4 minutes
C: 25 minutes	G: 12 minutes
D: 12 minutes	

Approximately, how many hours did Natasha spend helping customers?

1. 10 washes × $4.75 = $47.50. Jacqueline needs to wash her mother's car 11 times to save at least $49.

2. The total is about $15 (4 + 4 + 3 + 4).

3. You can purchase 6 cans with $10. Sample estimation strategy:

   I rounded $1.49 to $1.50. Two cans cost $3. Six cans cost $9. There is not enough money left to buy an extra can.

4. Yes, she has enough money. One possible mental strategy is to round to whole dollars: $4 + $7 + $4 = $15.

5. Dieter needs four one-meter pieces.

   Sample strategy: 2 × 49 cm is about 1 m (100 cm); 5 × 38 cm is about 2 m (200 cm). For 3 × 21 cm and 1 × 35 cm, he needs another one meter.

6. Natasha spent about two hours. Sample estimation strategy:

   14 + 7 + 21 + 12 minutes is about 50 minutes or a little less than one hour.

   38 + 14 + 12 minutes is a little over 60 minutes or one hour.

Decimal Point (page 1)

1. A school needs to purchase 513 new computers. If each computer costs $3,470, what is the total cost of these new computers? Use your calculator to solve this problem.

DO NOT use your calculator to solve the following problems. Instead, use your answer from problem 1 as a starting point to calculate the new results.

2. A ticket to the circus costs $5.13. If 347 people attended the circus, what is the total ticket revenue?

3. Every year, a ferryboat sails 3,470 times from the mainland to the island of Olku. The maximum number of passengers allowed on the ferry is 5,130. What is the maximum number of people that the boat can carry to the island each year?

4. Pierre pays $34.70 for one kilogram of specialty mushrooms. What would he pay for 5.13 kilograms of mushrooms?

5. Mr. Flores is making some of the costumes for the school play. He needs 51.3 yards of fabric, and the fabric costs $3.47 a yard. What is the total cost for the fabric?

1. $513 \times \$3,470 = \$1,780,110$

2. $\$5.13 \times 347 = \$1,780.11$ (divide answer by 100 and by 10 to compensate)

3. $5,130 \times 3,470 = 17,801,100$ (multiply answer by 10 to compensate)

4. $5.13 \times \$34.70 = \$178.011 \approx \$178.01$ (divide answer by 100 and by 100 to compensate)

5. $51.3 \times \$3.47 = \$178.011 = \$178.01$ (divide answer by 10 and 1000 to compensate)

Note: Students will have more success with this activity if they are familiar with decimals and powers of 10.

Probing questions:

How can you get from 513 to 51,300? to 51.3?

Use arrow language to summarize.

$$513 \xrightarrow{\quad ? \quad} 51,300$$

Decimal Point (page 2)

Louis used a calculator for his homework. Three minutes before handing in his work the next day, he notices that none of his answers has a decimal point. It is too late to re-do the work, so he decides to do each problem mentally. Do you think he can do this in two minutes?

How long does it take you? Time yourself and see how many you complete.

1. a. $6.25 \times 1.3 = 8125$

b. $25.1 \times 4.17 = 104667$

c. $2.125 \times 421.6 = 8959$

d. $0.85 \times 1.5 = 1275$

2. a. $384.75 \div 135 = 285$

b. $384.75 \div 13.5 = 285$

c. $384.75 \div 1.35 = 285$

d. $269.61 \div 28.5 = 946$

1. a. $6.25 \times 1.3 = 8.125$

    $6 \times 1 = 6$, which is less than 10 and certainly less than 81.

b. $25.1 \times 4.17 = 104.667$

    $25 \times 4 = 100$

c. $2.125 \times 421.6 = 895.9$

    $2 \times 400 = 800$

d. $0.85 \times 1.5 = 1.275$

    0.85 is less than one. $1 \times 1.5 = 1.5$

2. a. $384.75 \div 135 = 2.85$

    $300 \div 100 = 3$

b. $384.75 \div 13.5 = 28.5$

    I looked at the previous answer, $300 \div 10 = 30$.

c. $384.75 \div 1.35 = 285.$

    I looked at the previous answer, $300 \div 1 = 300$.

d. $269.61 \div 28.5 = 9.46$

    $280 \div 28 = 10$

Note: Students might wonder why someone would want to round 384 to 300. If you are rounding down the divisor, it is better to round down on the dividend. Ask students to think about this fair share situation.

There are 384 people attending a workshop. You have 135 experienced leaders. About how many people should go with each leader?

$384 \div 135$

If you consider $400 \div 100$, you would consider 4 people per leader, but in this situation, you are not using 35 of your leaders: 35 out of 135! In this situation, it would be best not to count all of the people attending. In this way, you will come closer to the actual calculation, which is actually less than 3.

Squares (page 1)

5^2 is a shorter notation for 5×5.

Somebody wrote this (we are not telling who!):

$13^2 = 13 \times 13$ $24^2 = 24 \times 24$
      $= 109$ $= 416$

1. Use your calculator to show that the two answers are wrong. What did this student do?

This large square consists of 13 small squares across by 13 small squares down.

2. a. Shade the parts of the large square that represent 10×10 and 3×3.

    b. If you think $13^2 = (10 \times 10) + (3 \times 3)$, you are really missing two parts. Write the number of small squares in those two parts.

    c. Add the numbers of small squares in the four parts. Is this equal to 13^2?

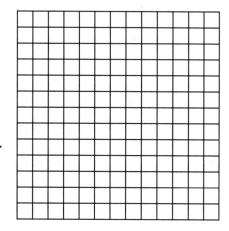

To find 24^2, you can think of a large square that consists of 24 times 24 small squares. You do not have to draw the small squares. You can imagine that they are there and write the dimensions of the four parts along outer edge. The drawing does not need to be to scale.

3. a. Write the number of small squares that would be in each of the four parts if they were all drawn.

    b. What is the answer to $24^2 =$_____?

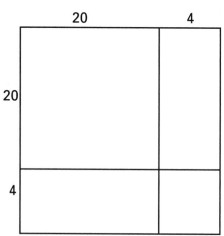

1. a. $13 \times 13 = 169$ $24 \times 24 = 576$

The first person multiplied 10×10 and added 3×3.

The second person only multiplied 20×20 and 4×4.

2. a. and **b.**

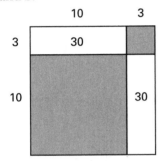

c. Yes. $(100 + 9 + 30 + 30 = 169$ squares)

The two shaded squares are $100 + 9$. The two small rectangles are $30 + 30$. Students can verify this with their answer for 1.

2. a.

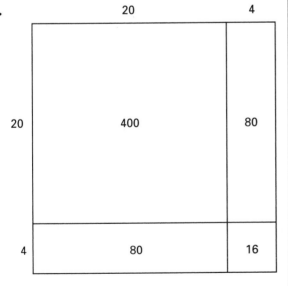

b. $24^2 = 576$; $(400 + 80 + 80 + 16 = 576)$

Squares (page 2)

3. a. Find the area of each of the four parts.

    b. What is the answer to 15^2?

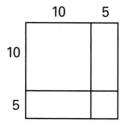

4. a. Find the area of each of the four parts.

    b. What is the answer to 25^2?

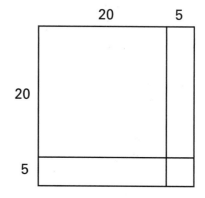

5. Find the answer to 35^2.

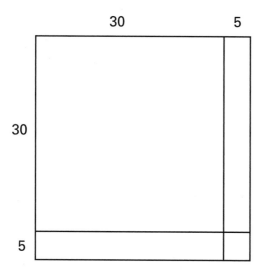

6. Find the answer to 45^2.

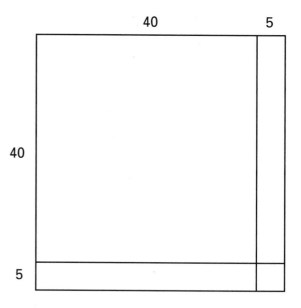

7. Find 55^2 and 65^2.

8. What pattern do you notice? How would you use this pattern to calculate 95^2?

3. a.

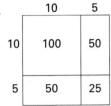

b. $15^2 = 225$; $(100 + 50 + 50 + 25 = 225)$

4. a.

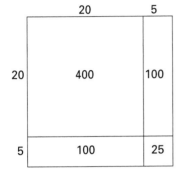

b. $25^2 = 625$; $(400 + 100 + 100 + 25 = 625)$

5. a.

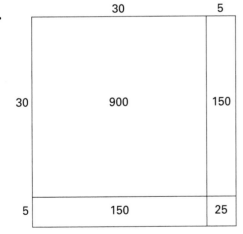

b. $35^2 = 1,225$; $(900 + 150 + 150 + 25 = 1,225)$

6. a.

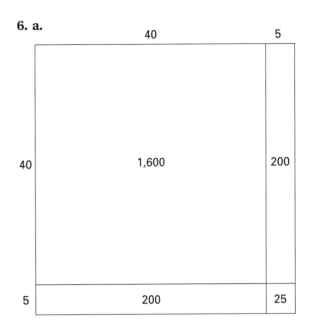

b. $45^2 = 2025$; $(1,600 + 200 + 200 + 25 = 2,025)$

7. $55^2 = 3,025$ $65^2 = 4,225$

8. Summarizing the results on this page to show one pattern:

$15^2 =$ 225
$25^2 =$ 625
$35^2 =$ 1225
$45^2 =$ 2025
$55^2 =$ 3025
$65^2 =$ 4225
$95^2 = 9,025$

Rectangles

1. What multiplication problem does this rectangle represent? Perform the calculation.

10 × 20	10 × 7
5 × 20	5 × 7

This rectangle is divided into four parts.

2. **a.** Fill in the missing numbers in each part.

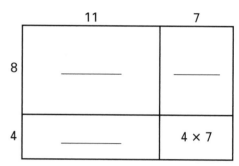

   b. Finish this number sentence showing the computation.

$$(8 + 4) \times (11 + 7)$$
$$= 8 \times 11 + 8 \times 7 + \underline{\hphantom{0}} \times \underline{\hphantom{0}} + \underline{\hphantom{0}} \times \underline{\hphantom{0}}$$
$$=$$
$$=$$

   c. Consider the number sentence showing this computation (10 + 2) × (10 + 8). How do you know, without computing, the answer is the same as in problem 2b?

3. Re-divide the rectangle in problem 2 so that you end up with the same answer, but use different numbers. Write the number sentence showing the computation.

1. The rectangle represents 15×27; vertically $10 + 5$ and horizontally $20 + 7$

2. a.

	11	7
8	8 × 11	8 × 7
4	4 × 11	4 × 7

  b. $(8 + 4) \times (11 + 7) =$

  $8 \times 11 + 8 \times 7 + 4 \times 11 + 4 \times 7 =$

  $88 + 56 + 44 + 28 = 216$

  c. $(10 + 2) \times (10 + 8)$ represents a 12×18 rectangle.

  The rectangle in 2b is the same size, since $8 + 4 = 12$ and $10 + 8 = 18$.

3. Here are two possible ways to re-divide the 12×18 rectangle.

  $(5 + 7) \times (12 + 6) =$

  $5 \times 12 + 5 \times 6 + 7 \times 12 + 7 \times 6 =$

  $60 + 30 + 84 + 42 = 216$

  $(9 + 3) \times (14 + 4) =$

  $9 \times 14 + 9 \times 4 + 3 \times 14 + 3 \times 4 =$

  $126 + 36 + 42 + 12 = 216$

Different Ways

Abraham and Beth mentally add 235 and 48; without using a calculator or a pencil and paper. Here is what they thought.

235 + 40 is 275:
275 + 8 is 283.

235 + 50 is 285.
It is too much. So
I must subtract 2.
285 − 2 is 283.

This arrow string shows Abraham's mental calculation.

$235 \xrightarrow{+40} 275 \xrightarrow{+8} 283$

1. Write an arrow string showing Beth's mental calculation.

2. Write two different arrow strings that you could use to mentally calculate 492 + 39.

3. Write two different arrow strings that you could use to mentally calculate each of the following problems.
   Be sure to include your answers.

a. 468 + 29 =		
b. 986 − 91 =		
c. 99 + 250 =		
d. 986 − 49 =		
e. 328 + 28 =		
f. 506 + 58 =		
g. 880 − 28 =		
h. 640 − 48 =		
i. 543 + 39 =		

Different Ways

1. Beth's method: 235 $\xrightarrow{+50}$ 285 $\xrightarrow{-2}$ 283

2. Possible arrow strings:

   492 $\xrightarrow{+40}$ 532 $\xrightarrow{-1}$ 531

   492 $\xrightarrow{+30}$ 522 $\xrightarrow{+9}$ 531

   500 $\xrightarrow{+39}$ 539 $\xrightarrow{-8}$ 531

   492 $\xrightarrow{+8}$ 500 $\xrightarrow{+31}$ 531

   492 $\xrightarrow{+8}$ 500 $\xrightarrow{+39}$ 539 $\xrightarrow{-8}$ 531

3. Sample arrow strings:

   a. 468 $\xrightarrow{+30}$ 498 $\xrightarrow{-1}$ 497

   468 $\xrightarrow{+20}$ 488 $\xrightarrow{+9}$ 497

   468 $\xrightarrow{+2}$ 470 $\xrightarrow{+27}$ 497

   b. 986 $\xrightarrow{-100}$ 886 $\xrightarrow{+9}$ 895

   986 $\xrightarrow{-86}$ 900 $\xrightarrow{-5}$ 895

   c. 250 $\xrightarrow{+100}$ 350 $\xrightarrow{-1}$ 349

   100 $\xrightarrow{+250}$ 350 $\xrightarrow{-1}$ 349

   d. 986 $\xrightarrow{-50}$ 936 $\xrightarrow{+1}$ 937

   986 $\xrightarrow{-46}$ 940 $\xrightarrow{-3}$ 937

   e. 328 $\xrightarrow{+30}$ 358 $\xrightarrow{-2}$ 356

   328 $\xrightarrow{+20}$ 348 $\xrightarrow{+8}$ 356

   328 $\xrightarrow{+2}$ 330 $\xrightarrow{+26}$ 356

   f. 506 $\xrightarrow{+60}$ 566 $\xrightarrow{-2}$ 564

   506 $\xrightarrow{+50}$ 556 $\xrightarrow{+8}$ 564

   g. 880 $\xrightarrow{-30}$ 850 $\xrightarrow{+2}$ 852

   880 $\xrightarrow{-20}$ 860 $\xrightarrow{-8}$ 852

   h. 640 $\xrightarrow{-40}$ 600 $\xrightarrow{-8}$ 592

   640 $\xrightarrow{-50}$ 590 $\xrightarrow{+2}$ 592

   i. 543 $\xrightarrow{+40}$ 583 $\xrightarrow{-1}$ 582

   543 $\xrightarrow{+30}$ 573 $\xrightarrow{+9}$ 582

Winning and Losing

Every day after school, Jesse plays marbles. Yesterday he started the day with 132 marbles and won 16 more. Today he lost nine marbles.

Each arrow string below shows a method for calculating the number of marbles that Jesse has now.

$$132 \xrightarrow{+\,16} 148 \xrightarrow{-\,9} 139$$
$$132 \xrightarrow{+\,10} 142 \xrightarrow{+\,6} 148 \xrightarrow{-\,10} 138 \xrightarrow{+\,1} 139$$
$$132 \xrightarrow{+\,7} 139$$

1. Explain why these three arrow strings show the number of marbles that Jesse has now.

Sometimes you can rewrite an arrow string to make the calculation easier. The new arrow string can be shorter or longer than the original but should yield the same result.

2. Here are some other marble results. Make a new arrow string so that it is easy to calculate the number of marbles. Complete the arrow string you created. Try to make some strings longer and others shorter (using only one arrow).

a. $35 \xrightarrow{+\,1,000} \underline{\quad} \xrightarrow{-\,800} \underline{\quad}$

e. $763 \xrightarrow{-\,98} \underline{\quad} \xrightarrow{+\,2} \underline{\quad}$

b. $800 \xrightarrow{+\,98} \underline{\quad} \xrightarrow{+\,100} \underline{\quad}$

f. $549 \xrightarrow{+\,31} \underline{\quad} \xrightarrow{-\,15} \underline{\quad}$

c. $589 \xrightarrow{-\,100} \underline{\quad} \xrightarrow{+\,199} \underline{\quad}$

g. $800 \xrightarrow{-\,100} \underline{\quad} \xrightarrow{+\,98} \underline{\quad}$

d. $763 \xrightarrow{-\,98} \underline{\quad} \xrightarrow{-\,2} \underline{\quad}$

h. $800 \xrightarrow{+\,98} \underline{\quad} \xrightarrow{-\,100} \underline{\quad}$

3. You may have written the same arrow string for problems **2g** and **2h**. Why are these strings essentially the same?

Sheila made this longer string for a subtraction problem.

$$637 \xrightarrow{-\,100} 537 \xrightarrow{+\,3} 540 \xrightarrow{+\,2} 542$$

4. What was her subtraction problem? $637 - \underline{\quad} = 542$

1. Adding 16 and then subtracting 9 is the same thing as adding 7, which is shown as the third arrow. Also 10 + 6 – 10 + 1 = 7, so the three arrow strings show the same thing.

2. Here are possible arrow strings that make the calculation easier. Note: Check to see if students make arrow strings that make the problem easier.

a. $35 \xrightarrow{+1,000} \ldots \xrightarrow{-800}$
   $35 \xrightarrow{+200} 235$

b. $800 \xrightarrow{+98} \ldots \xrightarrow{+100}$
   $800 \xrightarrow{+100} 900 \xrightarrow{+100}$
   $1,000 \xrightarrow{-2} 998$

c. $589 \xrightarrow{-100} \ldots \xrightarrow{+199}$
   $589 \xrightarrow{-100} 489 \xrightarrow{+200}$
   $689 \xrightarrow{-1} 688$

d. $763 \xrightarrow{-98} \ldots \xrightarrow{-2}$
   $763 \xrightarrow{-100} 663$

e. $763 \xrightarrow{-98} \ldots \xrightarrow{+2}$
   $763 \xrightarrow{-100} 663 \xrightarrow{+2} 665 \xrightarrow{+2} 667$

f. $549 \xrightarrow{+31} \ldots \xrightarrow{-15}$
   $549 \xrightarrow{+1} 550 \xrightarrow{+30} 580 \xrightarrow{-15} 565$
   $549 \xrightarrow{+1} 550 \xrightarrow{+15} 565$

g. $800 \xrightarrow{-100} \ldots \xrightarrow{+98}$
   $800 \xrightarrow{-2} 798$

h. $800 \xrightarrow{+98} \ldots \xrightarrow{-100}$
   $800 \xrightarrow{+100} 900 \xrightarrow{-100} 800 \xrightarrow{-2} 798$
   $800 \xrightarrow{-2} 798$

3. Adding 98 and then subtracting 100 produces the same answer as subtracting 100 and then adding 98. Both arrow strings can be rewritten as one arrow with – 2 above it. This problem shows that reversing the order of addition and subtraction does not alter the results. Note: Do not confuse this with the commutative property, which only works for addition and multiplication. 6 + 34 = 34 + 6, however, 6 – 34 is not the same as 34 – 6.

4. 637 – **95** = 542, because – 100 + 3 + 2 = 95

Multiplication and Division

Mr. Starks has an aquarium in his classroom. In order to find its volume, Mr. Starks's students first determine the aquarium's dimensions, as shown. Maya, Luisa, and Thomas each propose a different arrow string to find the aquarium's volume.

$60 \xrightarrow{\times\ 40} 2,400 \xrightarrow{\times\ 50} 120,000\ cm^3$

$60 \xrightarrow{\times\ 50} 3,000 \xrightarrow{\times\ 40} 120,000\ cm^3$

$60 \xrightarrow{\times\ 2,000} 120,000\ cm^3$

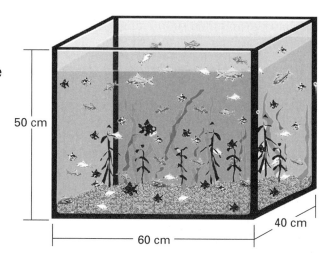

50 cm

60 cm

40 cm

1. Compare the three arrow strings. How are the strategies the same? How are they different?

2. For each of the following arrow strings fill in the missing numbers. Then write another arrow string that shows an alternative way to calculate the answer.

   a. $8 \xrightarrow{\times\ 5} \_\_\_ \xrightarrow{\times\ 4} \_\_\_$

   b. $32 \xrightarrow{\times\ 2} \_\_\_ \xrightarrow{\times\ 5} \_\_\_$

   c. $50 \xrightarrow{\times\ 5} \_\_\_ \xrightarrow{\div\ 4} \_\_\_$

   d. $750 \xrightarrow{\div\ 3} \_\_\_ \xrightarrow{\times\ 2} \_\_\_$

   e. $1,050 \xrightarrow{\div\ 5} \_\_\_ \xrightarrow{\div\ 2} \_\_\_$

   f. $9 \xrightarrow{\times\ 30} \_\_\_ \xrightarrow{\div\ 30} \_\_\_$

   g. $123 \xrightarrow{\times\ 100} \_\_\_ \xrightarrow{\times\ 5} \_\_\_$

3. Compare the following two arrow strings. Why are the final results different?

   $60 \xrightarrow{\times\ 5} \_\_\_ \xrightarrow{+\ 40} \_\_\_$ $60 \xrightarrow{+\ 40} \_\_\_ \xrightarrow{\times\ 5} \_\_\_$

1. All three arrow strings find the aquarium's volume; $60 \times 40 \times 50$ cm³. All arrow strings begin with 60. The first two have one of the other dimensions in the first arrow. The third string uses the product of the other dimensions for the first arrow: $40 \times 50 = 2,000$.

2. Sample responses:

   a. $8 \xrightarrow{\times 5} 40 \xrightarrow{\times 4} 160$

   $8 \xrightarrow{\times 4} 32 \xrightarrow{\times 5} 160$

   $8 \xrightarrow{\times 20} 160$

   b. $32 \xrightarrow{\times 2} 64 \xrightarrow{\times 5} 320$

   $32 \xrightarrow{\times 5} 160 \xrightarrow{\times 2} 320$

   $32 \xrightarrow{\times 10} 320$

   c. $50 \xrightarrow{\times 5} 250 \xrightarrow{\div 4} 62.5$

   $50 \xrightarrow{\div 4} 12.5 \xrightarrow{\times 5} 62.5$

   $50 \xrightarrow{\times \frac{5}{4}} 62.5$

   d. $750 \xrightarrow{\div 3} 250 \xrightarrow{\times 2} 500$

   $750 \xrightarrow{\times 2} 1,500 \xrightarrow{\div 3} 500$

   $750 \xrightarrow{\times \frac{2}{3}} 500$

   e. $1,050 \xrightarrow{\div 5} 210 \xrightarrow{\div 2} 105$

   $1,050 \xrightarrow{\div 2} 525 \xrightarrow{\div 5} 105$

   $1,050 \xrightarrow{\div 10} 105$

   f. $9 \xrightarrow{\times 30} 270 \xrightarrow{\div 30} 9$

   $9 \xrightarrow{\times 1} 9$

   g. $123 \xrightarrow{\times 100} 12,300 \xrightarrow{\times 5} 61,500$

   $123 \xrightarrow{\times 5} 615 \xrightarrow{\times 100} 61,500$

3. $60 \xrightarrow{\times 5} 300 \xrightarrow{+ 40} 340$

   $60 \xrightarrow{+ 40} 100 \xrightarrow{\times 5} 500$

The results of the arrow strings are different: 340 vs. 500. The results are different because the order in which you add and multiply is different. In the first arrow string, only the 60 is multiplied by 5 because the 40 is added on later. In the second arrow string, both 60 and 40 are multiplied by 5 because 40 is added on to 60 before the multiplication is done. Note: This is a way of revisiting order of operations.

Going Backwards

1. Find the result of each of the following arrow strings.

   a. $38 \xrightarrow{+2} \underline{\quad} \xrightarrow{\times 4} \underline{\quad} \xrightarrow{-20} \underline{\quad} \xrightarrow{\div 2} \underline{\quad}$

   b. $70 \xrightarrow{+50} \underline{\quad} \xrightarrow{-60} \underline{\quad} \xrightarrow{\times 3} \underline{\quad} \xrightarrow{-10} \underline{\quad}$

   c. $5 \xrightarrow{\times 20} \underline{\quad} \xrightarrow{-20} \underline{\quad} \xrightarrow{\times 2} \underline{\quad} \xrightarrow{\div 2} \underline{\quad}$

   d. $606 \xrightarrow{+14} \underline{\quad} \xrightarrow{\times 2} \underline{\quad} \xrightarrow{-100} \underline{\quad} \xrightarrow{+50} \underline{\quad}$

   e. $1,000 \xrightarrow{\div 4} \underline{\quad} \xrightarrow{\times 4} \underline{\quad} \xrightarrow{-500} \underline{\quad} \xrightarrow{+500} \underline{\quad}$

2. In each of the following arrow strings, the result is given. Fill in all of the missing numbers, especially the first number for each string.

   a. $\underline{\quad} \xrightarrow{\times 2} \underline{\quad} \xrightarrow{\div 4} \underline{\quad} \xrightarrow{-20} \underline{\quad} \xrightarrow{\times 7} 35$

   b. $\underline{\quad} \xrightarrow{+19} \underline{\quad} \xrightarrow{\times 2} \underline{\quad} \xrightarrow{-100} \underline{\quad} \xrightarrow{-95} 5$

   c. $\underline{\quad} \xrightarrow{+2} \underline{\quad} \xrightarrow{\times 2} \underline{\quad} \xrightarrow{-20} \underline{\quad} \xrightarrow{\div 2} 40$

   d. $\underline{\quad} \xrightarrow{+50} \underline{\quad} \xrightarrow{-10} \underline{\quad} \xrightarrow{\div 3} \underline{\quad} \xrightarrow{-2} 78$

   e. $\underline{\quad} \xrightarrow{+50} \underline{\quad} \xrightarrow{\div 2} \underline{\quad} \xrightarrow{-396} \underline{\quad} \xrightarrow{\times 4} 16$

3. Make up your own arrow strings with the following results and number of arrows.

   a. $\underline{\quad} \longrightarrow \underline{\quad} \longrightarrow \underline{\quad} \longrightarrow \underline{\quad} \longrightarrow 16$

   b. $\underline{\quad} \longrightarrow \underline{\quad} \longrightarrow \underline{\quad} \longrightarrow \underline{\quad} \longrightarrow 20$

   c. $\underline{\quad} \longrightarrow \underline{\quad} \longrightarrow \underline{\quad} \longrightarrow \underline{\quad} \longrightarrow 52$

4. Make up two arrow strings using other numbers, such as decimals or fractions or integers.

Mathematics in Context

1. a. $38 \xrightarrow{+2} 40 \xrightarrow{\times 4} 160 \xrightarrow{-20} 140 \xrightarrow{\div 2} 70$

b. $70 \xrightarrow{+50} 120 \xrightarrow{-60} 60 \xrightarrow{\times 3} 180 \xrightarrow{-10} 170$

c. $5 \xrightarrow{\times 20} 100 \xrightarrow{-20} 80 \xrightarrow{\times 2} 160 \xrightarrow{\div 2} 80$

or, since $\times 2$ and $\div 2$ can be cancelled out,

$5 \xrightarrow{\times 20} 100 \xrightarrow{-20} 80$

d. $606 \xrightarrow{+14} 620 \xrightarrow{\times 2} 1{,}240 \xrightarrow{-100}$ $1{,}140 \xrightarrow{+50} 1{,}190$

e. $1{,}000 \xrightarrow{\div 4} 250 \xrightarrow{\times 4} 1{,}000 \xrightarrow{-500}$ $500 \xrightarrow{+500} 1{,}000$

or, since $\div 4$ and $\times 4$ as well as -500 and $+500$ can be cancelled out, 1,000.

2. Note: The point of this exercise is to understand how to undo operations; addition undoes subtraction, multiplication undoes division, and vice versa. It is important for students to fully understand this; it will help them solve equations later in algebra. Try not to tell them how to work the arrow string backwards; allow them to make sense of this important process on their own timeline.

a. $50 \xleftarrow{\div 2} 100 \xleftarrow{\times 4} 25 \xleftarrow{+20} 5 \xleftarrow{\div 7} 35$

b. $81 \xleftarrow{-19} 100 \xleftarrow{\div 2} 200 \xleftarrow{+100}$ $100 \xleftarrow{+95} 5$

or

$81 \xleftarrow{+1} 80 \xleftarrow{-20} 100 \xleftarrow{\div 2}$ $200 \xleftarrow{+100} 100 \xleftarrow{+95} 5$

c. $48 \xleftarrow{-2} 50 \xleftarrow{\div 2} 100 \xleftarrow{+20} 80 \xleftarrow{\times 2} 40$

d. $200 \xleftarrow{-50} 250 \xleftarrow{+10} 240 \xleftarrow{\times 3} 80 \xleftarrow{+2} 78$

e. $750 \xleftarrow{-50} 800 \xleftarrow{\times 2} 400 \xleftarrow{+396} 4 \xleftarrow{\div 4} 16$

3. Sample arrow strings:

a. $35 \xrightarrow{+5} 40 \xrightarrow{\div 2} 20 \xrightarrow{-12} 8 \xrightarrow{\times 2} 16$

b. $25 \xrightarrow{\times 3} 75 \xrightarrow{\times 2} 150 \xrightarrow{+50} 200 \xrightarrow{\div 10} 20$

c. $5 \xrightarrow{-2} 3 \xrightarrow{\times 4} 12 \xrightarrow{+1} 13 \xrightarrow{\times 4} 52$

Note: Encourage students to check their answers for problem 3 by making reverse arrow strings.

4. Sample arrow strings:

Using operations with integers:

$-45 \xrightarrow{\div -5} 9 \xrightarrow{\times -11} -99 \xrightarrow{-1} -100$

Using operations with decimals:

$0.75 \xrightarrow{\div 0.25} 3 \xrightarrow{-4.6} -1.6 \xrightarrow{\div 0.4} -4$

Name _____ **Date** _____ **Class** _____

Decimals, Fractions, and Division

1. Eight Chess Club members purchased a new chess set for $6. How much was each member's share if everyone contributed the same amount? Explain how you solved this problem.

2. Six musicians play together on the street corner. Today they earn a total of $4 and decide to share the money equally. Joan and Juan want to find each musician's share. Here is how they each solve this problem.

Would you have solved this problem the way Joan did, the way Juan did, or in another way? Why?

3. Complete the table. You can use your calculator. Make up your own problem for the last row.

Division	Fraction	Decimal	Percent
5 ÷ 10			
		0.75	
			10%
2 ÷ 16			
	$\frac{1}{3}$		
			20%
		0.8	
	$\frac{3}{5}$		
15 ÷ 10			

Decimals, Fractions, and Division

1. Each member had to pay $0.75. Sample strategies:

   Eight members shared the cost for a $6 chess set. This is like four people sharing $3.

   One member's share is $\frac{1}{4}$ of $3, which is $\frac{3}{4}$ of $1. This is three quarters, or $0.75.

   $6 ÷ 8 members is $0.75 per member. This is $0.75.

2. Sample student opinions:

   I would have solved the problem like Joan because it is easier to use a calculator than to divide mentally.

   I would have solved the problem like Juan because I always solve money problems mentally.

   Note: Explain to students that the answer $0.67 comes from rounding 0.6666666 up to 0.67. To be precise, there is not enough money for all six musicians to get $0.67, because 6 × $0.67 = $4.02. Four musicians would get $0.67, and two would get $0.66.

3. The last row of the table will depend on the problem students choose.

Note: Have students check each other's answers in the last row. Be sure to point out that the division column can have the same numbers as the fraction column because a fraction represents division. For example, $\frac{5}{8}$ is the same as 5 ÷ 8. Also point out that the answers in the division and fraction columns can vary, as long as the fractions are equivalent.

Extension

Ask students to come up with multiple answers for the division and fraction columns in problem 3.

Division	Fraction	Decimal	Percent
5 ÷ 10	$\frac{5}{10}$ or $\frac{1}{2}$	0.5	50%
3 ÷ 4	$\frac{3}{4}$	0.75	75%
1 ÷ 10	$\frac{1}{10}$	0.1	10%
2 ÷ 16	$\frac{2}{16}$ or $\frac{1}{8}$	0.125	12.5%
1 ÷ 3	$\frac{1}{3}$	$0.\overline{33}$	$33\frac{1}{3}\% \approx 33.\overline{3}\%$
20 ÷ 100 or 2 ÷ 10 or 1 ÷ 5	$\frac{20}{100}$ or $\frac{2}{10}$ or $\frac{1}{5}$	0.2	20%
8 ÷ 10 or 4 ÷ 5	$\frac{80}{100}$ or $\frac{8}{10}$ or $\frac{4}{5}$	0.8	80%
3 ÷ 5	$\frac{3}{5}$	0.6	60%
15 ÷ 10	$\frac{15}{10}$ or $1\frac{5}{10}$ or $1\frac{1}{2}$	1.5	150%
1 ÷ 9	$\frac{1}{9}$	$0.1111\overline{1}$	$11\% \approx 11.\overline{1}\%$

Cleaning Up

Groups of students from Parker School help clean up the city parks.
They earn money by recycling glass bottles and aluminum cans.
Each different group shares the money equally.

1. How much money will each student earn in these situations?
Write your answers in two ways: as a fraction of a dollar and
as dollar amounts. Do not use your calculator.

	Fraction of a Dollar	Money Earned
a. $4 earned by five students		
b. $5 earned by four students		
c. $3 earned by four students		
d. $3 earned by eight students		
e. $6 earned by four students		
f. $6 earned by eight students		

2. If five people earn one dollar, each person gets $\frac{1}{5}$ of a dollar, or
20 cents. You can write this dollar amount as $0.20. If five people
earn three dollars, then each person gets $\frac{1}{5}$ of three dollars.
How much money is $\frac{1}{5}$ of three dollars? Write one share as a
fraction of one dollar.

3. Use your calculator to write each of the following amounts
of money.

a. $\frac{1}{8}$ of a dollar

b. $\frac{1}{3}$ of a dollar

c. $\frac{1}{4}$ of a dollar

d. $\frac{3}{5}$ of a dollar

e. $\frac{2}{3}$ of a dollar

f. $3\frac{3}{4}$ dollars

g. $2\frac{5}{6}$ dollars

h. $1\frac{5}{8}$ dollars

i. $9\frac{4}{5}$ dollars

j. $12\frac{3}{20}$ dollars

4. Without using your calculator, name the fraction for each decimal number.
When you are finished, use your calculator to check your answers.

a. 0.125

b. 0.25

c. 0.6

d. 0.666666667

e. 0.375

f. 0.75

g. 0.333333333

h. 0.8

i. 0.166666667

j. 0.111111111

Which problem was the easiest? Which was the most challenging?

Cleaning Up

1. Note: Answers have been rounded to the nearest cent.

   a. $\frac{4}{5}$ of a dollar, or $0.80

   b. $1\frac{1}{4}$ of a dollar, or $1.25

   c. $\frac{3}{4}$ of a dollar, or $0.75

   d. $\frac{3}{8}$ of a dollar, or $0.38

   e. $1\frac{1}{2}$ of a dollar, or $1.50

   f. $\frac{3}{4}$ of a dollar, or $0.75

Note: If students are having trouble, have them draw or use play money to act out the sharing situation. This exercise will help them develop a deep understanding of multiplication and division, and the relationship between the two operations.

For example, for $\frac{1}{5}$ of $4, students might find $\frac{1}{5}$ of $1 ($0.20) and multiply that by 4 ($0.80).

Others might split the first $3 in half, giving each person $0.50; there is $1.50 left for 5 people, so each gets an additional $0.30, for a total of $0.80.

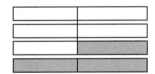

2. $\frac{1}{5}$ of $3 is $0.60. $\frac{1}{5}$ of $1 is $0.20, and $\frac{3}{5} = 3 \times \frac{1}{5}$; I calculated $3 \times \$0.20 = \$0.60$

3. Note: All answers are rounded to the nearest cent.

   a. $0.13   **e.** $0.67   **h.** $1.63

   b. $0.33   **f.** $3.75   **i.** $9.80

   c. $0.25   **g.** $2.83   **j.** $12.15

   d. $0.60

4. a. $\frac{1}{8}$ **e.** $\frac{3}{8}$ **h.** $\frac{4}{5}$

   b. $\frac{1}{4}$ **f.** $\frac{3}{4}$ **i.** $\frac{1}{6}$

   c. $\frac{3}{5}$ **g.** $\frac{1}{3}$ **j.** $\frac{1}{9}$

   d. $\frac{2}{3}$

Problems **b** and **f** are probably the easiest because of the relationship to money.

Problem **i** and **j** are probably the most challenging.

Note: If students think **a** and **e** are challenging, revisit the relationship between one-half, one-fourth, and one-eighth. (0.50, 0. 25, 0.125, half of 50 is 25, and half of 25 is 12.5) one-eighth and three eighths (0.125, 0.375).

Running for Class President (page 1)

At Cleveland Middle School, four students are running for the office of class president. The election will be held in two weeks, so they surveyed 600 students to determine which candidate is currently leading. The table shows the results of the survey.

Results of Class President Survey of 600 Students	
Candidate	Number of Votes
Tom Cooper	99
Liza Varelli	204
José da Gamba	153
Lucia Candelo	73
Undecided	71

1. Here are some statements about the survey results. Explain whether each statement is accurate or not accurate.

   a. About $\frac{1}{6}$ of the students say that they will vote for Tom Cooper.

   b. More than $\frac{1}{3}$ say that they will vote for Liza Varelli.

   c. About $\frac{1}{5}$ say that they will vote for José da Gamba.

   d. About $\frac{1}{8}$ say that they will vote for Lucia Candelo.

   e. More than $\frac{1}{6}$ say that they do not know how they will vote.

   f. About 33% of the students say that they will vote for Tom Cooper.

   g. Fewer than 20% say that they will vote for Liza Varelli.

   h. About 40% of the students say that they will vote for José da Gamba.

   i. More than 10% say that they will vote for Lucia Candelo.

   j. More than 20% say that they do not know how they will vote.

1. Sample estimation strategies:

a. True. One-sixth of 600 is 100; 99 is close to 100.

b. True. One-third of 600 is 200; 204 is more than 200.

c. False. One-fifth of 600 is 120; 153 is not about $\frac{1}{4}$.

d. True. One-eighth of 600 is 75; 73 is close to 75.

e. False. Seventy-one students do not know how they will vote; this is much less than 100 ($\frac{1}{6}$ of 600). 71 is more like $\frac{1}{8}$.

f. False. Thirty-three percent of 600 is about the same as $\frac{1}{3}$ of 600, or 200; this is much more than the 99 students that said that they will vote for Tom Cooper. 99 out of 66 is very close to $\frac{1}{6}$.

g. False. Twenty percent of 600 is the same as $\frac{1}{5}$ of 600, which is 120; this is much less than the 204 students that said that they will vote for Liza Varelli.

h. False. Since 20% of 600 is 120, 40% of 600 is 240; this is much more than the 153 students that said that they will vote for José da Gamba. 153 is about 25% of the students.

i. True. Ten percent of 600 is 60; 73 is just a little bit more than 60.

j. False. Seventy-one students said they do not know how they will vote; this is much less than 20% of 600 (120). It is more like 12%.

Running for Class President (page 2)

2. Use your calculator to determine the percent of students who will vote for each candidate and the percent of students who are still undecided.

3. Fill in the following pie chart to show the results of the survey. Choose a different color for each candidate and color in the legend and pie chart accordingly.

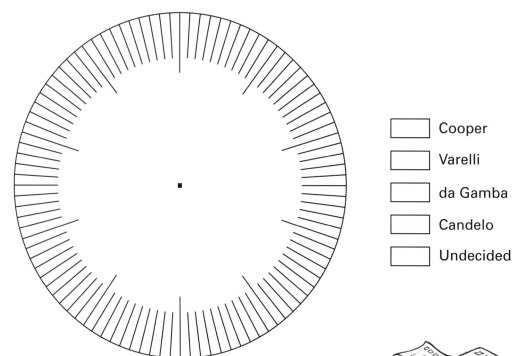

Cooper

Varelli

da Gamba

Candelo

Undecided

2.

Tom Cooper:	16.5% or about 17%
Liza Varelli:	34%
José da Gamba:	25.5% or about 26%
Lucia Candelo:	12.2% or about 12%
Undecided:	11.8% or about 12%

3.

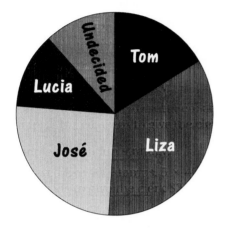

- ■ **Cooper**
- ▨ **Varelli**
- ▤ **da Gamba**
- ■ **Candelo**
- ▨ **Undecided**

Sale

B & B Fashion is having a sale. Stickers indicate the percent discount: 10%, 15%, 20%, 25%, $33\frac{1}{3}$%, or 50%.

The price tag on a sweater is $48, and a sticker shows a discount of 25%. Angela and David each use a different way to calculate the sale price.

A discount of 25% is the same as paying 75%, or $\frac{3}{4}$ of the price. One-fourth of $48.00 is $12.00. 3 × $12.00 = $36.00.

A discount of 25% is the same as $\frac{1}{4}$ off, or $12.00 off. $48.00 − $12.00 = $36.00.

Use either Angela's or David's method to calculate the sale price for each of the following items.

Item	Regular Price	Discount	Sale Price
Jacket	$96.00	25%	
Sweater	$48.00	$33\frac{1}{3}$%	
Jeans	$55.00	10%	
Shoes	$50.00	15%	
Winter Coat	$84.00	50%	
T-Shirt	$ 8.00	20%	
Shorts	$32.00	25%	
Pants	$72.00	$33\frac{1}{3}$%	
Skirt	$82.00	10%	
Dress Shirt	$48.00	25%	

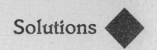

Sale

Item	Regular Price	Discount	Sale Price
Jacket	$96.00	25%	**$72.00**
Sweater	$48.00	$33\frac{1}{3}\%$	**$32.00**
Jeans	$55.00	10%	**$49.50**
Shoes	$50.00	15%	**$42.50**
Winter Coat	$84.00	50%	**$42.00**
T-Shirt	$ 8.00	20%	**$ 6.40**
Shorts	$32.00	25%	**$24.00**
Pants	$72.00	$33\frac{1}{3}\%$	**$48.00**
Skirt	$82.00	10%	**$73.80**
Dress Shirt	$48.00	25%	**$36.00**

Which Costs Less?

1. Soft Tunes and Audio Auction feature the same items but offer different discounts. Without using your calculator, circle which store has the lower sale price for each item featured. Be prepared to justify your selection.

Item	Regular Price	Soft Tunes Discount	Audio Auction Discount
CD Player	$360	25%	$70 off
Portable Stereo/ CD Player	$270	$33\frac{1}{3}\%$	$100 off
Speakers	$548	20%	$100 off
Stereo Cabinet	$598	15%	$100 off

2. Describe two ways to find 20% of $450.

3. Calculate each of the following.

a. 20% of $125

f. 25% of $320

b. 25% of $844

g. 10% of $529

c. $33\frac{1}{3}\%$ of $180

h. $66\frac{2}{3}\%$ of $690

d. 10% of $976

i. $33\frac{1}{3}\%$ of $219

e. 15% of $620

Note: You might want to copy the table and circle the store.

1. CD Player: Soft Tunes has the lower sale price because 25% off ($\frac{1}{4}$ off) $360 is $90. This is larger than the $70 discount offered by Audio Auction.

   Portable Stereo/CD Player: Audio Auction has the lower sale price of $100 off because the Soft Tunes sale price of $33\frac{1}{3}$% off ($\frac{1}{3}$ off) is only $90 off.

   Speakers: Soft Tunes has the lower sale price because 20% off ($\frac{1}{5}$ off) $548 is more than $100 (20% of $500).

   Stereo Cabinet: Audio Auction has the lower sale price of $100 off. If you round the regular price of $598 to $600, you can find 15% of $600 by first finding 10% of $600 ($60) and then adding on 5% of $600 ($30). Thus, the Soft Tunes discount is about $90 off.

2. Two strategies for finding 20% of $450:

   To find 20% of $450, you can find $\frac{1}{5}$ of $450, or just divide 450 by 5 to get 90.

   Since 20% is the same as 2 × 10%, 20% of $450 is equal to 2 × 10% × $450. Doing this calculation, I get 2 × $45, which equals $90.

3. a. $\frac{1}{5}$ × $125 = $25

   b. $\frac{1}{4}$ × $844 = $211

   c. $\frac{1}{3}$ × $180 = $60

   d. $\frac{1}{10}$ × $976 = $97.60

   e. 15% × $620 =
      (10% × $620) +
      (5% × $620) =
      $62 + $31 = $93

   f. $\frac{1}{4}$ × $320 = $80

   g. $\frac{1}{10}$ × $529 = $52.90

   h. $\frac{2}{3}$ × $690 =
      2 × $\frac{1}{3}$ × $690 =
      2 × $230 = $460

   i. $\frac{1}{3}$ × $219 = $73

Note: Encourage students to do problem 3 mentally.

On the Number Line

For each number line, find the number indicated by the arrow. For each number line, the marks are the same distance apart.

1.

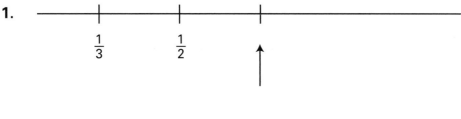

_____

2.

_____

3.

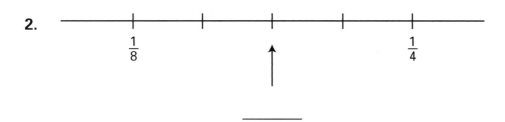

_____

4.

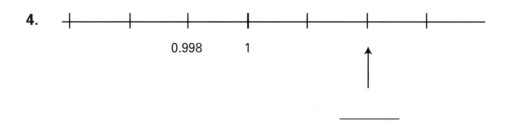

_____

Mathematics in Context

1.

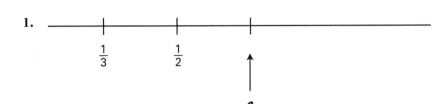

Note that $\frac{1}{3} = \frac{2}{6}$ and $\frac{1}{2} = \frac{3}{6}$. The fraction $\frac{3}{6}$ is in the middle between $\frac{2}{6}$ and $\frac{4}{6}$, so the arrow indicates $\frac{4}{6}$ or $\frac{2}{3}$.

2.

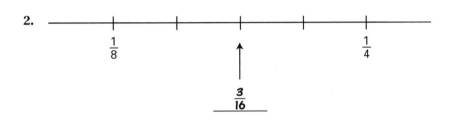

Note that you are looking for a fraction that is in the middle between $\frac{1}{8}$ and $\frac{1}{4}$ or $\frac{2}{8}$. To find this fraction, you have to double the denominator again; in the middle between $\frac{1}{8} = \frac{2}{16}$ and $\frac{2}{8} = \frac{4}{16}$ is the fraction $\frac{3}{16}$.

3.

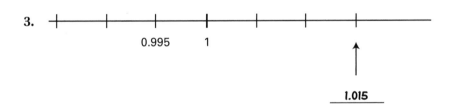

Note that the steps indicated on the number line are 0.005.

4.

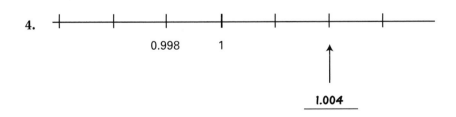

Note that the steps indicated on the number line are 0.002.

Name _____ Date_____ Class_____

Comparing Two Schools (page 1)

At Greenfield Middle School, $\frac{2}{3}$ of the students are female.
At Brendel Middle School, $\frac{5}{8}$ of the students are female.
To determine which school has a larger fraction of female
students you can think of two bars with the same
number of segments. Here you can use 24 segments.

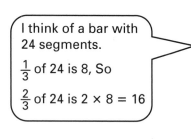

I think of a bar with
24 segments.

$\frac{1}{3}$ of 24 is 8, So

$\frac{2}{3}$ of 24 is 2 × 8 = 16

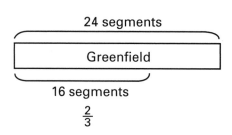

24 segments

Greenfield

16 segments

$\frac{2}{3}$

24 segments

Brendel

1. a. Complete the bar for Brendel Middle School.

   b. Which school has the larger fraction of female
      students?

   c. Why are 24 segments handy? What other
      number of segments would have worked too?

_____ segments

2. For each of the following categories, determine
    which school has the larger fraction of students.

   a. Students Transported by Bus

      Greenfield, $\frac{5}{6}$ of the students

      Brendel, $\frac{3}{4}$ of the students

   b. Seventh-Grade Students

      Greenfield, $\frac{1}{4}$ of the students

      Brendel, $\frac{2}{5}$ of the students

1. a. $\frac{1}{8}$ of 24 segments is 3 segments, so $\frac{5}{8}$ of 24 segments is 15 segments.

b. Greenfield Middle School has the larger fraction of female students.

In the Greenfield bar, 16 out of 24 segments are shaded.

In the Brendel bar 15 out of 24 segments are shaded.

Greenfield : $\frac{16}{24}$

Brendel : $\frac{15}{24}$

Note that students do not have to draw all segments; they should just indicate the number of segments for each bar.

c. 24 segments is handy since you need to divide the bars into a number of segments that is divisible by both 3 and 8, such as 24.

Another number of segments that would work is any multiple of 24, for example, 48.

2. Students Transported by Bus

Greenfield has the larger fraction of students transported by bus.

Note: Students need to indicate that the bars need to be divided into a number of segments that is divisible by both 6 and 4, such as 12. They do not have to draw all segments.

Greenfield : $\frac{10}{12}$

Brendel : $\frac{9}{12}$

Seventh-Grade Students

Brendel has the larger fraction of sixth-grade students.

Note: Students need to indicate that bars need to be divided into a number of segments that is divisible by both 4 and 5, such as 20. They do not have to draw all segments.

Greenfield : $\frac{5}{20}$

Brendel : $\frac{8}{20}$

Comparing Two Schools (page 2)

Gina uses a ratio table to compare fractions. Here is her work for comparing $\frac{5}{6}$ and $\frac{3}{4}$.

$\frac{5}{6}$:

Part	5	10	
Whole	6	12	

$\frac{3}{4}$:

Part	3	6	9
Whole	4	8	12

3. Compare her ratio table strategy with the segmented bars you used to solve problem 2a on the previous page. What do you notice?

4. Compare the following pairs of fractions and circle the larger fraction. You may choose any strategy you like. Show your work or reasoning.

a. $\frac{1}{4}$ and $\frac{1}{5}$

b. $\frac{2}{3}$ and $\frac{5}{8}$

c. $\frac{2}{3}$ and $\frac{4}{9}$

d. $\frac{1}{3}$ and $\frac{2}{5}$

e. $\frac{2}{3}$ and $\frac{1}{2}$

f. $\frac{3}{8}$ and $\frac{1}{4}$

g. $\frac{3}{4}$ and $\frac{4}{5}$

h. $\frac{3}{5}$ and $\frac{3}{4}$

i. $\frac{4}{9}$ and $\frac{1}{3}$

3. Sample student strategy:

It's the same idea. Gina divided up the fractions into smaller parts until the numbers on the bottom (the denominators) matched. I was trying to do the same thing using the segmented bars, except I had to get the number of segmented bars to match to compare the two fractions.

Note: Students may reason in a variety of ways. Discuss different strategies in class.

Many possible strategies are presented for 4a. These strategies as well as others may also be used for the other problems.

4. a. $\frac{1}{4}$ is the larger fraction.

- I compared the parts of 20; $\frac{1}{4}$ of 20 is 5, whereas $\frac{1}{5}$ of 20 is only 4.

- I calculated $1 \div 4 = 0.25$ and $1 \div 5 = 0.2$ with my calculator.

- I thought of dividing a pie that needs to be divided. If you get $\frac{1}{4}$ of it, you get a larger piece than if you get $\frac{1}{5}$ of it.

  I thought of two bars, divided in 20 parts. For $\frac{1}{4}$ you shade 5 parts and for $\frac{1}{5}$ you shade 4 bars, which is less.

b. $\frac{2}{3}$ is the larger fraction.

c. $\frac{2}{3}$ is the larger fraction.

d. $\frac{2}{5}$ is the larger fraction.

e. $\frac{2}{3}$ is the larger fraction.

f. $\frac{3}{8}$ is the larger fraction.

g. $\frac{4}{5}$ is the larger fraction.

h. $\frac{3}{4}$ is the larger fraction.

i. $\frac{4}{9}$ is the larger fraction.

Name _____ Date_____ Class_____

What Difference?

Among Ms. Washington's students, $\frac{2}{3}$ of the class participate in a sport. Of those students, one-fourth of them play basketball. What fraction of Ms. Washington's class participates in a sport other than basketball? Here is how Thomas solved this problem.

I think of a class with 24 students. Then $\frac{2}{3}$ of 24 is 16, so 16 students play sports.

And $\frac{1}{4}$ of 16 is 4, so 4 play basketball.

That means that 12 play another sport, and 12 out of 24 is the same as $\frac{1}{2}$, so the answer is $\frac{1}{2}$.

24 students

12 play sports

4 play basketball

1. Among Mr. Guiford's students, $\frac{3}{4}$ of the class participate in a sport. If $\frac{1}{3}$ of those students play basketball, what fraction of the class participates in a sport other than basketball?

2. At Jefferson Middle School, $\frac{1}{3}$ of the students study a foreign language. If $\frac{2}{9}$ of the students study Japanese, what fraction of the students study a foreign language other than Japanese?

3. Solve the following subtraction problems.

   a. $\frac{3}{8} - \frac{1}{4} =$ f. $\frac{6}{8} - \frac{2}{3} =$

   b. $\frac{5}{8} - \frac{2}{4} =$ g. $\frac{2}{3} - \frac{1}{2} =$

   c. $\frac{1}{4} - \frac{1}{6} =$ h. $\frac{4}{8} - \frac{3}{9} =$

   d. $\frac{4}{5} - \frac{2}{3} =$ i. $\frac{4}{9} - \frac{2}{6} =$

   e. $\frac{2}{3} - \frac{2}{5} =$

1. Five-twelfths of the students participate in a sport other than basketball. Sample strategy:

If the class has 12 students, then nine of them participate in sports and four of them play basketball. This means that five of the students play a sport other than basketball, so the answer is $\frac{5}{12}$.

2. One-ninth of the students study a foreign language other than Japanese. Sample strategy:

Draw a bar with nine segments to represent a class of nine students. One-third of nine segments is three segments, and $\frac{2}{9}$ of nine segments is two segments. The difference is one segment, so the answer is $\frac{1}{9}$.

3. a. $\frac{3}{8} - \frac{1}{4} = \frac{1}{8}$. Sample strategy:

Draw a bar with eight segments. Three-eighths of eight segments is three segments, and $\frac{1}{4}$ of eight segments is two segments. The difference is one segment, so the answer is $\frac{1}{8}$.

b. $\frac{5}{8} - \frac{2}{4} = \frac{1}{8}$. Sample strategy:

Draw a bar with eight segments. Five-eighths of eight segments is five segments, and $\frac{2}{4}$ of eight segments is four segments. The difference is one segment, so the answer is $\frac{1}{8}$.

c. $\frac{1}{4} - \frac{1}{6} = \frac{1}{12}$. Sample strategy:

Draw a bar with 12 segments. One-fourth of 12 segments is three segments, and $\frac{1}{6}$ of 12 segments is two segments. The difference is one segment, so the answer is $\frac{1}{12}$.

d. $\frac{4}{5} - \frac{2}{3} = \frac{12}{15} - \frac{10}{15} = \frac{2}{15}$

e. $\frac{2}{3} - \frac{2}{5} = \frac{10}{15} - \frac{6}{15} = \frac{4}{15}$

f. $\frac{6}{8} - \frac{2}{3} = \frac{18}{24} - \frac{16}{24} = \frac{2}{24} = \frac{1}{12}$

g. $\frac{2}{3} - \frac{1}{2} = \frac{4}{6} - \frac{3}{6} = \frac{1}{6}$

h. $\frac{4}{8} - \frac{3}{9} = \frac{36}{72} - \frac{24}{72} = \frac{12}{72} = \frac{3}{18} = \frac{1}{6}$

i. $\frac{4}{9} - \frac{2}{6} = \frac{8}{18} - \frac{6}{18} = \frac{2}{18} = \frac{1}{9}$

Note: Encourage students to use their own strategy to solve the problems.

Many Zeros

Words	Numeral
One Thousand	1,000
One Million	1,000,000
One Billion	1,000,000,000
One Trillion	1,000,000,000,000

1. Write the following numbers as a numeral using digits.

a. thirteen million _____

b. 2 billion _____

c. one and a half million _____

d. 1.4 million _____

e. 2.3 billion _____

2. And now the other way around, write each number in words.

a. 7,000,000 _____

b. 9,000,000,000 _____

c. 15,000,000 _____

d. 1,500,000 _____

e. 5,000,000,000 _____

f. 500,000 _____

3. Make up a similar writing exercise. Exchange with a classmate and do each other's problems.

1. **a.** 13,000,000

   b. 2,000,000,000

   c. 1,500,000

   d. 1,400,000

   e. 2,300,000,000

2. **a.** seven million

   b. nine billion

   c. fifteen million

   d. one and a half million

   e. five billion

   f. five hundred thousand

3. Have students check each other's writing exercises.

On the Number Line

Here are some population data.

1. Next to each label, write the population as numeral using digits.

Australia
19.9 million

Spain
40.3 million

United States
293.0 million

Canada
32.5 million

Cyprus
$\frac{1}{4}$ million

Mexico
105.9 million

World
6.5 billion

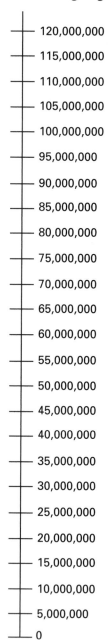

120,000,000
115,000,000
110,000,000
105,000,000
100,000,000
95,000,000
90,000,000
85,000,000
80,000,000
75,000,000
70,000,000
65,000,000
60,000,000
55,000,000
50,000,000
45,000,000
40,000,000
35,000,000
30,000,000
25,000,000
20,000,000
15,000,000
10,000,000
5,000,000
0

Source: http://www.census.gov

2. Connect each label to the correct place on the number line. For two labels, this will not be possible; the number line is not long enough.

3. On top of this page, paste a blank sheet of paper. Then extend the number line so that you can connect the label of the United States.

4. Look now at the label of the WORLD. How many extra sheets of paper do you need to connect this label? Explain your answer.

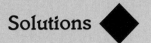
1. Australia   19,900,000 inhabitants

   Spain   40,300,000

   United States   293,000,000

   Canada   32,500,000

   Cyprus   250,000

   Mexico   105,900,000

   World   6,500,000,000

3. If you double the number line, you will have two times 120 million or 240 million. For the United States, you will need about half the length more of the number line to locate it below 300 million.

4. The number line on the original sheet ends at 120,000,000. The world population is 6,500,000,000, which is about 50 times as much. You would need over 50 sheets of paper to locate the world population on the number line.

2.

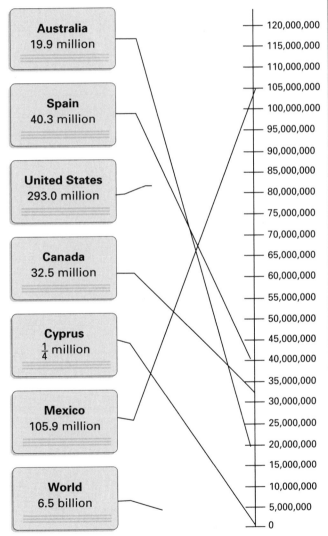

Years, Days, Hours, Seconds

Suppose it is your birthday. People will probably ask how old you are, and your answer will be a certain number of years. How would you answer in terms of days, hours, and/or seconds? Use a calculator to answer the following problems. If the calculator's display is too small for all of the digits, devise another way to answer the problems.

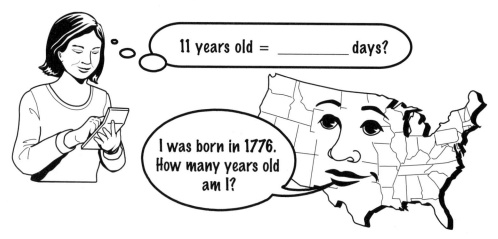

11 years old = _____ days?

I was born in 1776. How many years old am I?

1. How old will you be in years on your next birthday?

2. How old will you be in days on your next birthday?

3. How old will you be in hours on your next birthday?

4. How many years old will the United States be on its next Independence Day? (Hint: The United States became independent in 1776.)

5. How many hours old will the United States be on its next Independence Day?

I can count to one million!

OK, I wanna hear that!

6. How long would this take? Explain your answer, or show your work.

7. How many seconds old will you be on your 60th birthday?

1. Answers will vary depending on the age of the student.

2.–3. Answers will vary depending on the age of the student. Three sample solutions:

2. 10th Birthday

10 years $\xrightarrow{\times 365}$ 3,650 days

11th Birthday

11 years $\xrightarrow{\times 365}$ 4,015 days

12th Birthday

12 years $\xrightarrow{\times 365}$ 4,380 days

3. 10th Birthday

3,650 days $\xrightarrow{\times 24}$ 87,600 hours

11th Birthday

4,015 days $\xrightarrow{\times 24}$ 96,360 hours

12th Birthday

4,380 days $\xrightarrow{\times 24}$ 105,120 hours

4.–5.

Answers depend on the current year. Here are answers for the 2006–2007 school year:

4. 230 years old (2006 − 1776 = 230)

5. 2,014,800 hr (230 years $\xrightarrow{\times 365}$ ... days $\xrightarrow{\times 24}$ ... hours)

6. Note: To estimate how fast one can count, students can do a little experiment, by starting at 6,700 and counting one minute, or counting ten numbers and measuring how long this will take. An estimate that you can count a number per second is a little too optimistic. Sample student explanation:

Suppose it is possible to count one number per two seconds, you need two million seconds.

2,000,000 sec $\xrightarrow{\div 60}$ 33,333 $\frac{1}{3}$ min $\xrightarrow{\div 60}$

(about) 555.6 hours $\xrightarrow{\div 24}$ (about) 23 days

7. 60 $\xrightarrow{\times 365}$ 21,9000 $\xrightarrow{\times 24}$ 525,600 $\xrightarrow{\times 60}$

31,536,000 $\xrightarrow{\times 60}$ 1,892,160,000

Note: Advise students not to consider leap years when doing these problems. The suggestion for an Extension problem includes the consideration of leap years.

Also, advise students not to consider what time of the day it is right now, rather to solve the problems asking about hours and seconds assuming that it is the exact time at which the student or country was born.

Extension

To peak the interest of advanced students, you can have them consider leap years in solving the problems. Every year divisible by four is a leap year, except most century years. The year 2000 was not a leap year. The only century years that are leap years are those divisible by 400 but not by 4,000. Leap years have 366 days, since February has an extra day.

Rounding (page 1)

Here is data on passenger traffic from some of the world's airports. The data is ordered alphabetically.

1. a. Make a top ten list, ordered by number of passengers.

b. For each city on this top ten list, round the number of passengers to a whole number of millions.

	City (Airport)	Total Passengers
1	Atlanta (ATL)	79,086,792
2	Amsterdam (AMS)	39,960,400
3	Bangkok (BKK)	30,175,379
4	Chicago (ORD)	69,508,672
5	Dallas/Fort Worth (DFW)	53,253,607
6	Denver (DEN)	37,505,138
7	Detroit (DTW)	32,664,620
8	Frankfurt/Main (FRA)	48,351,664
9	Hong Kong (HKG)	27,092,290
10	Houston (IAH)	34,154,574
11	Las Vegas (LAS)	36,285,932
12	London (LGW)	30,007,021
13	London/Heathrow (LHR)	63,487,136
14	Los Angeles (LAX)	54,982 838
15	Madrid (MAD)	35,854,293
16	Miami (MIA)	29,595,618
17	Minneapolis/St. Paul (MSP)	33 201,860
18	New York (JFK)	31,732,371
19	Newark (EWR)	29,431,061
20	Orlando (MCO)	27 319,223
21	Paris (CDG)	48,220,436
22	Philadelphia (PHL)	24,671,075
23	Phoenix (PHX)	37,412,165
24	Rome (FCO)	26,284,478
25	San Francisco (SFO)	29,313,271
26	Seattle (SEA)	26 755,888
27	Sydney (SYD)	25,333,508
28	Tokyo (HND)	62,876,269
29	Tokyo (NRT)	26,537,406
30	Toronto (YYZ)	24,739,312

http://www.airports.org

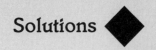
1. a. and **b.** Top ten list, ordered by number of passengers. In the third column, the numbers are rounded to whole millions.

City (Airport)	Total Passengers	Total Passengers in Millions
Atlanta (ATL)	79,086,792	79
Chicago (ORD)	69,508,672	70
London/Heathrow (LHR)	63,487,136	63
Tokyo (HND)	62,876,269	63
Los Angeles (LAX)	54,982,838	55
Dallas/Fort Worth (DFW)	53,253,607	53
Frankfurt/Main (FRA)	48,351,664	48
Paris (CDG)	48,220,436	48
Amsterdam (AMS)	39,960,400	40
Denver (DEN)	37,505,138	38

Rounding (page 2)

Denver (DEN) had 37,505,138 passengers. You can round this number using a unit of millions: 37,505,138 is about 37.5 million, rounded to the nearest tenth of a million.

2. PHOENIX (PHX) had 37,412,165 passengers. How many million is this? Round this number to the nearest tenth of a million, (one decimal).

3. Which of the following numbers would round to 37.5 million? Explain your answer.

   a. 37,505,876

   b. 37,598,652

   c. 37,389,989

   d. 37,456,789

4. Find the lowest and the highest number of passengers that would round to 37.5 million.

5. Round the following prices to cents.
   a. $11.435

   b. $326.6249

   c. $2865.996

   d. $21.445

Naomi bought a T-shirt. When her mother asked her what she paid for it, she answered, "Oh, about 20 dollars."

6. a. Name one possible price of Naomi's T-shirt.

   b. Name the lowest and the highest possible price for Naomi's T-shirt. You may assume that Naomi rounded the price to a whole number of dollars.

Mathematics in Context

2. Phoenix had 37.4 million passengers.

3. Both part **a** and part **d** round to 37.5 million.

   a. 37.5 million

   b. 37.6 million

   c. 37.4 millio

   d. 37.5 million

4. Lowest number of passengers: 37,450,000

   Highest number of passengers: 37,549,999

5. a. $11.44

   b. $326.62

   c. $2866.00

   d. $21.45

6. a. Student answers may vary. A reasonable price is $19.98.

   b. Lowest price: $19.50

      Highest price: $20.49

Track Your Time and Accuracy (page 1)

Do each problem as quickly as you can.

Record your Start Time: [   ]

1. a. 10 × 28 =

   b. 5 × 28 =

2. a. 2 × 5 × 7 =

   b. 2 × 18 × 5 =

3. a. 10 × 30 =

   b. 20 × 30 =

4. a. 10 × 3.1 =

   b. 100 × 3.1 =

5. a. 3 × 30 =

   b. 6 × 15 =

6. a. 10 × 15 =

   b. 11 × 15 =

7. a. 10 × 25 =

   b. 9 × 25 =

8. a. 40 ÷ 10 =

   b. 4 ÷ 10 =

9. a. 6 × 15 =

   b. 8 × 45 =

10. a. 1.2 × ____ = 12

    b. 1.2 × ____ = 6

Record Your Finish Time: [   ]

Fill in your results. Keep track of your results.
With practice, you will improve both your speed
and accuracy.

My Results:

Total Time

_____

Total Correct

_____

1. **a.** 280
   b. 140

2. **a.** 70
   b. 180

3. **a.** 300
   b. 600

4. **a.** 31
   b. 310

5. **a.** 90
   b. 90

6. **a.** 150
   b. 165

7. **a.** 250
   b. 225

8. **a.** 4
   b. 0.4

9. **a.** 90
   b. 360

   Possible strategies:

   $8 \times 45 = 4(2 \times 45) = 4 \times 90 = 360$

   or

   $8 \times 45 = 10 \times 45 - 2 \times 45 = 450 - 90 = 360$

10. **a.** 10
    b. 5

Track Your Time and Accuracy (page 2)

Do each problem as quickly as you can.

Record your Start Time: [   ]

1. a. 10 × 23 =

  b. 20 × 23 =

2. a. 4 × 60 =

  b. 8 × 60 =

3. a. 10 × 21 =

  b. 20 × 21 =

4. a. 2 × 5 × 9 =

  b. 2 × 17 × 5 =

5. a. 10 × 5.2 =

  b. 100 × 5.2 =

6. a. 10 × 25 =

  b. 11 × 25 =

7. a. 10 × 15 =

  b. 9 × 15 =

8. a. 60 ÷ 10 =

  b. 6 ÷ 10 =

9. a. 6 × 25 =

  b. 8 × 35 =

10. a. 1.4 × ____ = 14

  b. 1.4 × ____ = 7

Record your Finish Time: [   ]

Fill in your results. Keep track of your results. With practice, you will improve both your speed and accuracy.

My Results:

Total Time

_____

Total Correct

_____

1. **a.** 230
   b. 460

2. **a.** 240
   b. 480

3. **a.** 210
   b. 420

4. **a.** 90
   b. 170

5. **a.** 52
   b. 520

6. **a.** 250
   b. 275

7. **a.** 150
   b. 135

8. **a.** 6
   b. 0.6

9. **a.** 150
   b. 280

10. **a.** 10
    b. 5

Track Your Time and Accuracy (page 3)

1. a. Create ten problems similar to the previous problems. Of course, you have to provide the answers to your problems.

b. Exchange your problems with a classmate.

c. Keep a clean copy of your problems so that you can exchange problems with a classmate whenever there is time. Continue to keep a record of your improvements in speed and accuracy. You may want to record your scores in a table and graph the results.

Record your Start Time:

Record your Finish Time:

My Results:

Total Time

Total Correct

1. Students' problems will vary. Have students check each other's results.

Ways to Write Numbers (page 1)

	Numbers						
Arabic Numerals	1	9	10	19	38	93	100
Roman Numerals	I	IX	X	XIX	XXXVIII	XCIII	C
English Words	one	nine	ten	nineteen	thirty-eight	ninety-three	one hundred
French Words	un	neuf	dix	dix-neuf	trente-huit	quatrevingt-treize	cent
Spanish Words	uno	nueve	diez	diecinueve	treinta y ocho	noventa y tres	cien
Portuguese Words	um	nove	dez	dezanove	trinta e oito	noventa e três	cem

1. Use the information in this table to describe similarities and differences in the way numbers are written.

Our Number System is a positional system, which uses the digits 0 through 9. The first base unit is ten. You can compose all of the numbers using a base of ten.

Most of the numbers between ten and twenty have names that reflect the addition operation. *Eleven* and *twelve* are exceptions; these words do not reflect the addition operation.

Name	Composition
thir-teen	3 + 10
four-teen	4 + 10
fif-teen	?

2. How would you compose *for-ty*, and *six-ty*?

To compose numbers larger than nineteen, you need to use a combination of operations. For example, thirty-four is composed of 3 tens and 4 ones: 3 × 10 + 4; seven hundred thirty-four is composed of 7 hundreds, 3 tens, and 4 ones: 7 × 100 + 3 × 10 + 4.

3. Write each number word as a numeral and as a composition reflecting the words.

Word Name	Numeral	Composition
a. five hundred sixty-five		
b. two hundred fifty		
c. three thousand five hundred		
d. thirty-five hundred		

1. Here are sample descriptions; you might have students work in groups to create a combined list of comparisons of numbers in the four languages for class discussion.

Similarities and Differences

- The words for numbers 1 and 9 are similar across all languages.

- The word for 10 looks alike in French, Spanish, and Portuguese, but it is different in English. English uses a similar word to measure a ten-year time span, the word *decade*.

- All four languages have a word for 19 that uses some root of both 9 and 10; however, the English language appears to blend them together, whereas the other languages have a distinct separator with the Spanish and Portuguese using an AND conjunction implying the addition operation.

- All four languages have a word for 38 that is made as 30 and 8.

- English, Spanish, and Portuguese each have a word for 93 that is composed as 90 and 3, but the French word for 93 uses a connection to twenty: "four twenties and thirteen" or $4 \times 20 + 13$.

- In French, Spanish, and Portuguese the words for 100 are similar, but the word is different in English. English has a similar word to measure a hundred-year time span, the word *century*.

Extension

If there are students in your class who speak yet another language, compare the way numbers are pronounced in their language as well. How are words for numbers in this language different from English?

2. 40 is 4×10 and 60 is 6×10.

3.

Word Name	Numeral	Composition
a. five hundred sixty-five	565	$5 \times 100 + 6 \times 10 + 5$
b. two hundred fifty	250	$2 \times 100 + 5 \times 10$
c. three thousand five hundred	3,500	$3 \times 1,000 + 5 \times 100$
d. thirty-five hundred	3,500	35×100

Ways to Write Numbers (page 2)

4. Compare your answers to **c** and **d**. What do you notice?

5. a. What is a different word name for one thousand nine hundred fifty?

   b. Write two different number compositions for both word names.

Hank volunteers at the homeless shelter. Hank's job today is to place 350 free meal coupons into envelopes, with 10 coupons in each envelope.

6. a. How many envelopes will Hank fill today?

   b. Yesterday, Hank placed 2,351 meal coupons into envelopes. How many envelopes did he fill yesterday?

Hank places the extra coupon(s) in an envelope and marks it "partial."

   c. What fractional part of an envelope is this? What decimal part of an envelope is this?

   d. What if Hank fills each envelop with 100 coupons? How would your answers for **a**, **b**, and **c** change?

There are many ways to describe the number 2,351. A common way to describe 2,351 is to expand it: 2 thousands, 3 hundreds, 5 tens, and 1 ones.
Here are some other ways to describe 2,351.

thousands	hundreds	tens	ones
2	3	5	1

2,351 is 2,351 ones.   2,351 is 23.51 hundreds.
2,351 is 235.1 tens.   2,351 is 2.351 thousands.

7. a. Explain these five different ways to describe 2,351.
   b. Describe the number 350 in four different ways.
   c. Describe the number 15,387 in six different ways.

8. Write one numeral for each number word description.
   a. 6 thousands, 9 hundreds, and 5 ones
   b. 5.673 thousands   **d.** 34.76 hundreds
   c. 3,478.9 tens   **e.** 125.5 hundreds

4. The numeral for both three thousand five hundred and thirty-five hundred is the same, but you might not have used the comma as a separator for **d**. The compositions reflect the words, but produce the same result.

5. **a**. nineteen hundred fifty

   b. $1 \times 1{,}000 + 9 \times 100 + 5 \times 10$ or $19 \times 100 + 5 \times 10$

6. **a**. 35 full envelopes

   b. 235 full envelopes

   c. $\frac{1}{10}$ of a full envelope or 0.1 of a full envelope

   d. With 100 coupons per envelope:
   - 3 full envelopes
   - 23 full envelopes
   - $\frac{51}{100}$ of a full envelope or 0.51 of a full envelope

7. **a.** Sample response:

   The first way is the typical way to expand the number to match the place value column name. The other four ways describe how you can group the number into piles. For example, if you take 2,351 and group into piles of ten, you would have 235 piles and another with only 0.1 of a pile of ten; so 2,351 is 235.1 tens. Grouping in piles of a hundred, thousands, and ones produces the others.

   Note: Some students might notice a pattern. The location of the decimal point is after the column of groups you are making.

   ↓
   2,3**5**1 is 235.1 tens, 5 was in the tens place.

   ↓
   2**3**51 is 23.51 hundreds, 3 was the hundreds place.

   ↓
   2,351 is 2.351 thousands, 2 was in the thousands place.

If they notice this pattern, ask them to explain why this works. You might make Dienes blocks available to students to help them with their explanations. Dienes blocks provide a visual representation of the relationship between columns in the base ten system. When you partition a number into groups of tens, hundreds, thousands, etc., you end up with that many groups.

   b. 350
   - 350 is 3 hundreds, 5 tens, and no ones
   - 350 is 35 tens
   - 350 is 3.5 hundreds
   - 350 is 350 ones

   c. 15,387
   - 15,387 is 15,387 ones
   - 15,387 is 1,538.7 tens
   - 15,387 is 153.87 hundreds
   - 15,387 is 15.387 thousands
   - 15,387 is 1.5387 ten-thousands
   - 15,387 is 1 ten-thousand, 5 thousands, 3 hundreds, 8 tens, and 7 ones

8 **a.** 6,905

   b. 5,673

   c. 34,789

   d. 3,476

   e. 12,550

Powers of Ten (page 1)

Our number system is based on powers of ten. You can use powers of 10 as a shortcut to describe numbers. Recall that 100 is 10 × 10 or 10^2, read as "ten to the second power," or "ten squared."

For most powers of ten, we have special names, but not for all.

$10^2 = 10 \times 10 = 100$, or one hundred

$10^3 = 10 \times 10 \times 10 = 1,000$, or one thousand

The next special name is one million, which is 1,000,000, or 10^6.

1. a. In the table on the next page you see the names for large numbers. Write these numbers as powers of ten.

b. What pattern do the powers of ten have?

You can describe each number in the table that is larger than 1,000 as a power of 1,000. For example, 1,000,000 is 1,000 × 1,000, or $1,000^2$.

2. Fill in the last column of the table.

3. Calculate the following products. Write your answers as a power of ten.

a. 10 × 1,000 =

b. 1,000 × 1,000 =

c. 1,000 × 1,000 × 1,000 =

d. 100^2 =

e. $100^2 \times 100^2$ =

f. $10^4 \times 10^3$ =

g. $10^3 \times 10^2 \times 10$ =

4. Calculate the following quotients. Write your answers as a power of ten.

a. 1,000,000 ÷ 1,000 =

b. 1,000,000,000 ÷ 1,000 =

c. 1,000 ÷ 10 =

d. $10^6 \div 10$ =

e. $10^8 \div 10^3$ =

f. $10^{10} \div 10^5$ =

g. $10^3 \div 10^3$ =

1. a. See chart on next page. Note: You might discuss patterns in the table.

  b. After $1,000 = 10^3$, the powers of 10 go up by three so that they are all multiples of three.

2. See chart on next page.

3. Answer   Strategy:

  a. 10^4 $10 \times 1,000 = 10,000$

  b. 10^6 $1,000 \times 1,000 = 1,000,000$

  c. 10^9 $1,000 \times 1,000 \times 1,000 =$ $1,000,000,000$

  d. 10^4 100^2 is 100×100 or $10,000$

  e. 10^8 Using previous problem, $100^2 \times 100^2$ is $10^4 \times 10^4$ or 10^8

  f. 10^7 $10^4 \times 10^3$

  g. 10^6 $10^3 \times 10^2 \times 10$

4. Answer   Problem/Solution

  a. 10^3 $1,000,000 \div 1,000 = 1,000$

  b. 10^6 $1,000,000,000 \div 1,000 = 1,000,000$

  c. 10^2 $1,000 \div 10 = 100$

  d. 10^5 $10^6 \div 10$; one million divided by ten is one hundred thousand.

  e. 10^5 $10^8 \div 10^3$; one hundred million divided by one thousand is one hundred thousand.

  f. 10^5 $10^{10} \div 10^5$; ten billion divided by one hundred thousand is one hundred thousand.

  g. 10^0 $10^3 \div 10^3$; any nonzero number divided by itself is 1 which is 10^0.

Note: For some students, you may need to review more on properties of exponents:

$10^0 = 1$

$10^1 = 10$

10^2 means 10×10 so $10^2 = 100$

In 10^2, ten is the base and 2 is the exponent.

The exponent tells how many times to repeat the base as a factor.

10^3 means $10 \times 10 \times 10$, so $10^3 = 1,000$.

Powers of Ten (page 2)

as Numeral	in Words	Power of 10	Power of 1,000
10	ten		
100	hundred		
1,000	thousand		
1,000,000	million		$1,000^2$
1,000,000,000	billion		
1,000,000,000,000	trillion		
	quadrillion		
	quintillion		
	sextillion		
	septillion		
	octillion		
	nonillion		
	decillion		
	undecillion		
	duodecillion		
	tredecillion		
	quattuordecillion		
	quindecillion		
	sexdecillion		
	septendecillion		
	octodecillion		
	novemdecillion		
	vigintillion		
	unvigintillion		
	duovigintillion		
	trevigintillion		
	quattuorvigintillion		
	quinvigintillion		

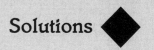
as Numeral	in Words	Power of 10	Power of 1,000
10	ten	10^1	
100	hundred	10^2	
1,000	thousand	10^3	
1,000,000	million	10^6	$1,000^2$
1,000,000,000	billion	10^9	$1,000^3$
1,000,000,000,000	trillion	10^{12}	$1,000^4$
	quadrillion	10^{15}	$1,000^5$
	quintillion	10^{18}	$1,000^6$
	sextillion	10^{21}	$1,000^7$
	septillion	10^{24}	$1,000^8$
	octillion	10^{27}	$1,000^9$
	nonillion	10^{30}	$1,000^{10}$
	decillion	10^{33}	$1,000^{11}$
	undecillion	10^{36}	$1,000^{12}$
	duodecillion	10^{39}	$1,000^{13}$
	tredecillion	10^{42}	$1,000^{14}$
	quattuordecillion	10^{45}	$1,000^{15}$
	quindecillion	10^{48}	$1,000^{16}$
	sexdecillion	10^{51}	$1,000^{17}$
	septendecillion	10^{54}	$1,000^{18}$
	octodecillion	10^{57}	$1,000^{19}$
	novemdecillion	10^{60}	$1,000^{20}$
	vigintillion	10^{63}	$1,000^{21}$
	unvigintillion	10^{66}	$1,000^{22}$
	duovigintillion	10^{69}	$1,000^{23}$
	trevigintillion	10^{72}	$1,000^{24}$
	quattuorvigintillion	10^{75}	$1,000^{25}$
	quinvigintillion	10^{78}	$1,000^{26}$

More Powers

You can write 2 million as the product of a number and a power of ten: 2×10^6.

1. For the following problems, write your answers as a product of a number and a power of ten.

a. 2 million + 3 million

b. 2 billion + 1.5 billion

c. 7.5 thousand − 3.5 thousand

d. $2 \times 10^3 + 5 \times 10^3$

e. $3 \times 10^6 - 1.5 \times 10^6$

f. 500,000 + 1 million

g. $20 \times 10^5 + 4 \times 10^6$

Here are four different strategies to add 2 million and 5 thousand.

Ayla
2 million is equal to 2,000 thousand, so 2,000 thousand + 5 thousand = 2,005 thousand or $2{,}005 \times 10^3$

Carlo
$2 \times 10^6 + 5 \times 10^3 =$ $2{,}000 \times 10^3 + 5 \times 10^3 =$ $2{,}005 \times 10^3$

Brad
$2 \times 10^6 + 5 \times 10^3 =$ $2 \times 10^6 + 0.005 \times 10^6 =$ 2.005×10^6

Felicia
$2{,}000{,}000 + 5{,}000 =$ $2{,}005{,}000 =$ 2.005×10^6

2. a. Compare these four strategies. How are they different? How are they the same?

b. Which strategy do you like the most? Why?

3. Write your answers as a product of a number and a power of ten. Use two different strategies.

a. 5 million + 20 thousand

b. 7 billion + 400 million

c. $3 \times 10^3 + 7 \times 10^4$

d. $5.0 \times 10^7 - 6.5 \times 10^5$

Mathematics in Context

1. Students answers might be different from these but must be equivalent.

   a. 5 million, which is 5×10^6

   b. 3.5 billion, which is 3,500,000,000 or 3.5×10^9 or 35×10^8

   c. 4 thousand, which is $4 \times 1,000$ or 4×10^3

   d. 7×10^3, 2 thousand + 5 thousand is 7 thousand

   e. 1.5×10^6, 3 million – 1.5 million is 1.5 million.

   f. 1.5×10^6 or 15×10^5, 0.5 million + 1 million is 1.5 million or 1,500,000

   g. 6×10^6, $20 \times 10^5 + 4 \times 10^6$

   20 hundred thousand + 4 million

   2 million + 4 million is 6 million.

Note: When scientific notation is used, the first number is always less than 10.
This means 3.5×10^9 is scientific notation, but 350×10^7 is not.

2. **a.** Sample response:

   The strategies are different because some students worked with thousands and others worked with millions. Some students liked to use words and then translate into powers of ten at the end while others like to work with powers of ten first.

   For example:

   • Ayla changes 2 million into 2,000 thousands, so she can add thousands.

   • Brad likes to work with millions, but he uses powers of tens instead of words.

   • Carlo, like Ayla, likes to use thousands, but like Brad he uses powers of tens instead of words.

   • Felicia writes the entire numeral and then combines them and finally writes it as a power of 10.

   The strategies are the same because they all make use of powers of ten.

   b. Answers will depend on student choices.

   Have students explain to one another why they prefer the strategy they chose. You might want to revisit this question after they do problem 3.

3. Two different strategies are shown for each problem, but students may have chosen yet another strategy.

	Strategy I	Strategy II
a.	5 million + 20 thousand 5,000 thousand + 20 thousand 5,020 thousand $5,020 \times 10^3$	5 million + 20 thousand 5,000,000 + 20,000 5,020,000 5.02 million or 5.02×10^6
b.	7 billion + 400 million 7,000 million + 400 million 7,400 million $7,400 \times 10^6$	7 billion + 400 million $7 \times 10^9 + 400 \times 10^6$ $7 \times 10^9 + 4 \times 10^8$ $7 \times 10^9 + 0.4 \times 10^9$ 7.4×10^9
c.	$3 \times 10^3 + 7 \times 10^4$ $0.3 \times 10^4 + 7 \times 10^4$ 7.3×10^4	$3 \times 10^3 + 7 \times 10^4$ 3 thousand + 70 thousand 73 thousand or 73×10^3
d.	$5.0 \times 10^7 - 6.5 \times 10^5$ $500 \times 10^5 - 6.5 \times 10^5$ 493.5×10^5	$5.0 \times 10^7 - 6.5 \times 10^5$ $5.0 \times 10^7 - 0.065 \times 10^7$ 4.935×10^7

Units (page 1)

Here are two different rulers. One is marked with inches and the other with centimeters.

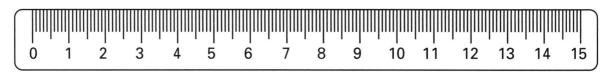

1. a. Which ruler—the first or the second—shows centimeters? How do you know?

   b. Both the centimeter and inch are partitioned into smaller units. Compare and contrast these partitions. Which one is based on units of ten?

2. You may use the two rulers to complete:

   a. one inch is about _____ centimeters.

   b. one centimeter is about _____ inch.

3. How long is one meter? Look around you. Is there anything in the classroom that is about one meter long or wide or high?

4. Compare a meter stick with a yardstick. Which one is based on units of ten?

5. Leo states that a meter is approximately 10% longer than a yard. Is he right? Explain.

A centimeter (cm) is one-hundredth of a meter (m).

There are two different ways to describe this relationship, with a fraction and with a decimal.

   $1 \text{ cm} = \frac{1}{100} \text{ m}$ $1 \text{ cm} = 0.01 \text{ m}$

6. Describe each of the following relationships in two ways, with a fraction and with a decimal.

Fraction	**Decimal**
a. 2 cm = _____ m	2 cm = _____ m
b. __ cm = $\frac{1}{2}$ m	__ cm = _____ m
c. 25 cm = _____ m	25 cm = _____ m
d. 7.5 cm = _____ m	7.5 cm = _____ m

Mathematics in Context

1. a. The second ruler shows centimeters. You can tell because centimeters are smaller than inches.

b. The centimeters are divided into 10 intervals, whereas the inches are divided into 16 intervals. Centimeters are based on units of ten.

2. a. 1 inch is about 2.5 centimeters

b. 1 centimeter is about 0.4 inch or less than one-half inch

3. One meter is 100 centimeters.Students may say that the teacher's desk is almost a meter high, and so on.

4. A meter is a little more than 3 inches longer than one yard.

One yard measures 0.9144 m, or one meter equals 1.0936 yards. The meter is based on units of ten.

5. Leo is right. Sample explanation:

One meter equals 100 cm. 10% of 1 meter is 10 cm. One yard equals 0.9 m, or 90 cm, which is indeed a difference of about 10%.

6. a. $2 \text{ cm} = \frac{2}{100} \text{ m};$ $\quad 2 \text{ cm} = 0.02 \text{ m}$

b. $50 \text{ cm} = \frac{1}{2} \text{ m};$ $\quad 50 \text{ cm} = 0.5 \text{ m}$

c. $25 \text{ cm} = \frac{1}{4} \text{ m};$ $\quad 25 \text{ cm} = 0.25 \text{ m}$

d. $7.5 \text{ cm} = \frac{75}{1000} \text{ m};$ $\quad 7.5 \text{ cm} = 0.075 \text{ m}$

Note that metric units are usually abbreviated; for example millimeter (mm), decimeter (dm), kilometer (km).

$$1 \text{ mm} \xrightarrow{\times\,10} 1 \text{ cm} \xrightarrow{\times\,10} 1 \text{ dm} \xrightarrow{\times\,10} 1 \text{ m}$$

$$1 \text{ inch} \xrightarrow{\times\,12} 1 \text{ foot} \xrightarrow{\times\,3} 1 \text{ yard}$$

The metric system is based on units of 10. It is easier to convert units in the metric system. For example, 25 cm = 0.25 meters.

One millimeter is one-thousandth of a meter. You can write 25 mm as 25 × 1 mm or 25 × 0.001m, so 25 mm = 0.025 m.

In the Customary System, there are too many relationships to remember, and they are not based on units of 10. For example, 25 in = ... yards.

One inch is one thirty-sixth of a yard. You can write 25 inches as 25 × 1 inch or 25 × 0.2776 yard, so 25 in = 0.6944 yard.

This is not a very good decimal number to remember for changing units. There will also be problems because of rounding errors.

Units (page 2)

The height of this MP3 player is one decimeter.

This height is drawn in its actual size.

7. a. How many centimeters is this?

b. How many decimeters are in one meter?

8. Use two different ways to describe the relationship between a decimeter and a meter, with a fraction and with a decimal.

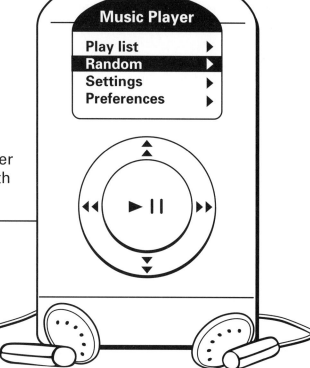

Millimeters, centimeters, decimeters, and **meters** are metric units used to measure length.

The prefixes, *deci*, *centi*, and *milli*, are derived from Latin.

Deci means one-tenth.

One decimeter (dm) is one-tenth of a meter (m).

Centi means one-hundredth.

One centimeter (cm) is one-hundredth of a meter.

Milli means one-thousandth.

One millimeter (mm) is one-thousandth of a meter.

9. Describe each of the following relationships in two ways, with a fraction and with a decimal.

Fraction	Decimal
a. 1 mm = _____ m	1 mm = _____ m
b. 1 mm = _____ cm	1 mm = _____ cm
c. 3 dm = _____ m	3 dm = _____ m
d. 2.5 cm = _____ dm	2.5 cm = _____ dm
e. 7.5 mm = _____ cm	7.5 mm = _____ cm

Mathematics in Context

7. a. One decimeter equals 10 centimeters

   b. 10 decimeters equal 1 meter

8. 1 dm = $\frac{1}{10}$ m;   1 dm = 0.1 m

9. a. 1 mm = $\frac{1}{1000}$ m;   1 mm = 0.001 m

   b. 1 mm = $\frac{1}{10}$ cm;   1 mm = 0.1 cm

   c. 3 dm = $\frac{3}{10}$ m;   3 dm = 0.3 m

   d. 2.5 cm = $\frac{25}{100}$ dm;   2.5 cm = 0.25 dm

   e. 7.5 mm = $\frac{75}{100}$ cm;   7.5 mm = 0.75 cm

Units (page 3)

In the United States, most people use the Customary System rather than the metric system. The inch (in.) is a unit for measuring length in the Customary System.

1. What other measurement units for length do you know? And for weight? And volume?

2. Complete these sentences with the appropriate unit.

   a. The width of a door is about 1 _____ .

   b. The height of my bicycle is about 20 _____ .

   c. The length of the hallway is about 30 _____.

   d. The small town is about 2 _____ wide.

Here is a ruler with inches.

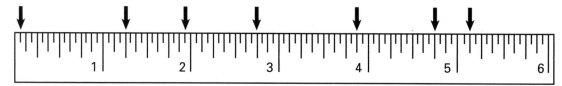

3. **a.** How do you know that this ruler is not based on units of ten?

   b. How is each inch partitioned?

   c. Use a mixed number to write the number of inches indicated by each arrow. Use the abbreviation, ", for inches.

4. Calculate each sum. Remember that 12 in. = 1 ft. The abbreviation, ', is for feet.

   a. $2\frac{1}{2}'' + 1\frac{1}{4}'' =$ **c.** $7'\, 2\frac{3}{4}'' + 11'\, 5\frac{1}{4}'' =$

   b. $1\frac{1}{8}'' + \frac{3}{4}'' + 2\frac{1}{2}'' =$ **d.** $12'\, 9'' + 13'\, 2\frac{1}{2}'' + 5'\, 3\frac{3}{4}'' =$

5. Write each length in a different form.

   a. 5 ft 7 in. = _____ in.   **c.** $3\frac{2}{3}$ yd = _____ ft

   b. 75 in. = _____ ft _____ in.   **d.** $10\frac{1}{3}$ yd = _____ in.

1. Sample answers: foot, yard, and mile for length; ounce (oz) and pound (lb) for weight; and gallon for volume.

2. **a.** yard

   b. inches

   c. feet or yards

   d. miles

3. **a.** One inch is not divided into ten smaller parts.

   b. First one inch is divided into four parts of $\frac{1}{4}$ inch. The next division is in parts of $\frac{1}{8}$ of an inch and the smallest parts are $\frac{1}{16}$ of an inch.

   c. $\frac{1}{16}''$; $1\frac{1}{4}''$; $1\frac{15}{16}''$; $2\frac{3}{4}''$; $3\frac{7}{8}''$; $4\frac{3}{4}''$; $5\frac{1}{8}''$

4. **a.** $3\frac{3}{4}''$

   b. $4\frac{3}{8}''$

   c. $18'8''$

   d. $31'3\frac{1}{4}''$

5. **a.** 67 in.

   b. 6 ft 3 in.

   c. 11 ft

   d. 372 in.

Metric System (page 1)

There are three base units in the metric system; the meter for length, the gram for weight or mass, and the liter for volume or capacity.

Multiples and fractions of these units are created by adding prefixes to the names of the defined units. For example, the prefix **kilo** means one thousand, so 1 **kilo**meter is 1,000 meters.

Prefix	Symbol	Meaning		in Words
		as a Number	as a Power of Ten	
Tera-	T-			Trillion
Giga-	G-			Billion
Mega-	M-			Million
Kilo-	k-			Thousand
Hecto-	h-	100	10^2	Hundred
Deca-	da-	10	10^1	Ten
Base Unit:				**Measures:**
Meter	m	1	10^0	Length
Gram	g	1		Weight
Liter	l	1		Volume
Deci-	d-	0.1	10^{-1}	Tenth
Centi-	c-	0.01		Hundredth
Milli-	m-	0.001		Thousandth
Micro-	μ-			Millionth
Nano-	n-			Billionth
Pico-	p-			Trillionth

1. Write five measurement units that have one of these prefixes and explain how it compares to its basic unit of meter, gram, or liter.

2. Write each prefix as a number by filling in the third column.

3. **a.** Write each prefix as a power of ten by filling in the fourth column.

   b. What pattern do you notice in the fourth column, Meaning as a Power of Ten?

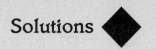
1. Here are some examples, but students only need five measurement relationships.

kilometer (km)	1,000 meters
megameter (Mm)	1,000,000 meters
gigameter (Gm)	1,000,000,000 meters
terameter (Tm)	1,000,000,000,000 meters
micrometer	one millionth of a meter
nanometer	one billionth of a meter
picometer	one trillionth of a meter
deciliter	one tenth of a liter
centiliter	one hundredth of a liter
hectoliter	100 liters
milligram	one thousandth of a gram
hectogram	100 grams

2. Third column of table.

Prefix	Symbol	Meaning			
		as a Number	as a Power of Ten	in Words	
Tera	T	1,000,000,000,000	10^{12}	Trillion	
Giga	G	1,000,000,000	10^9	Billion	
Mega	M	1,000,000	10^6	Million	
Kilo	k	1,000	10^3	Thousand	
Hecto	h	100	10^2	Hundred	
Deca	da	10	10^1	Ten	
Base Unit:					
Meter	m	1	10^0	Length	
Gram	g	1		Weight	
Liter	l	1		Volume	
Deci	d	0.1	10^{-1}	Tenth	
Centi	c	0.01	10^{-2}	Hundredth	
Milli	m	0.001	10^{-3}	Thousandth	
Micro	μ	0.000001	10^{-6}	Millionth	
Nano	n	0.000000001	10^{-9}	Billionth	
Pico	p	0.000000000001	10^{-12}	Trillionth	

The origins of these prefixes are quite interesting because each section of sizes has been adopted from a different language. The prefixes for very large multipliers—*tera, giga,* and *mega*–come from Greek. The small magnitude multipliers–*kilo, hecto, deca, deci,* and *centi*–all come from French. We took *milli* from Latin, surprisingly the only prefix taken from this once widespread language. The next range of fractional multipliers–*micro* and *nano*–also come from Greek. The large fractional multipliers were defined later than the others, and pulled from other languages. We took *pico* from Spanish and *femto* from Danish.

[Source: http://gaga.essortment.com/metricsystempr_rbya.htm]

3. a. See the fourth column of the table shown in problem 2.

b. From ten to one thousand the powers increase by one; from tenths to thousandths, the powers decrease by one.

From million to trillion, the powers increase by three; from millionths to trillionths the powers decrease by three.

Metric System (page 2)

4. Fill in the correct prefix, written out fully and abbreviated.

a. My pencil is about 150 _____ meters (___ m).

b. The circumference of the earth is about 40,000 _____ meters (___ m).

c. A hair grows approximately 0.3 _____ meters (___ m) a day.

d. A door height is about 200 _____ meters (___ m).

Five decimeters is five-tenths of a meter. Here are three ways to write this relationship.

5 dm = $\frac{5}{10}$ meter, as a fraction;

5 dm = 0.5 meter, as a decimal; and

5 dm = 5×10^{-1} meter, as a product of a number and a power of 10.

5. Describe each of the following relationships in three ways: as a fraction, as a decimal, and as a product of a number and a power of ten.

	Fraction	Decimal	Product (# × 10)
a. 5 cm			
b. 7 dm			
c. 15 mm			

You can see how small a millimeter is by looking at a centimeter ruler. How small is a micrometer?

6. Do you think you can see something of the size of one micrometer (μm)? Explain why or why not.

The size of a virus is between 0.02 and 0.25 μm.

7. Convert these measures to millimeters.

Nanotechnology is a branch of engineering that develops and uses devices that have sizes of only a few nanometers. Nanotechnology is sometimes called molecular manufacturing.

8. What fraction of a millimeter is one nanometer?

4. a. milli (mm)

   b. kilo (km)

   c. milli (mm)

   d. centi (cm)

5.

		Fraction	Decimal	Product (# × 10)
a.	5 cm	$\frac{5}{100}$ m	0.05 m	5×10^{-2} m
b.	7 dm	$\frac{7}{10}$ m	0.7 m	7×10^{-1} m
c.	15 mm	$\frac{15}{1,000}$ m	0.015 m	15×10^{-3} m

6. No, you cannot see something of the size of one micrometer. Sample explanation:

One micrometer is 0.000001 or one millionth of a meter, which equals 0.001 mm or one thousandth of a millimeter.

7. The size of the virus is between 0.00002 mm and 0.00025 mm. Sample explanation:

1 μm is 0.001 mm, so to convert, you multiply by 0.001.

0.02 μm = 0.00002 mm

0.25 μm = 0.00025 mm

8. 1 nm = $\frac{1}{1,000,000}$ mm.

One nanometer (see table on previous page) is one billionth of a meter, or $\frac{1}{1,000,000,000}$ m. To convert to mm, you multiply by 1,000:

$$1,000 \times \frac{1}{1,000,000,000} = \frac{1}{1,000,000}$$

A Little about Liters

Here is a graduated cylinder. You can measure the volume of a liquid by reading the water level. The markings on the cylinder indicate that you can measure up to one liter of liquid.

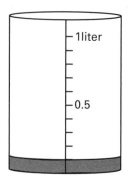

1. What is the water level of this cylinder? What is the volume of the liquid?

2. What interval markings would you want on the cylinder if you had to measure 0.07 liter of liquid?

Milliliters (mL), centiliters (cL), deciliters (dL), and **liters(L)** are metric units used to measure liquid volume.

milli means one-thousandth   one milliliter = $\frac{1}{1000}$ liter

centi means one-hundredth   one centiliter = $\frac{1}{100}$ liter

deci means one-tenth   one deciliter = $\frac{1}{10}$ liter

---

3. A tin can holds 0.33 liter of lemonade. Mark the level on this graduated cylinder to show 0.33 liter of lemonade.

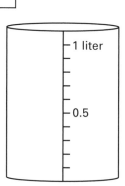

4. **a.** How much is 0.33 liter in deciliters?

   0.33 liter = ____ deciliters

   b. How much is 0.33 liter in centiliters?

   0.33 liter = ____ centiliters

   c. How much is 0.33 liter in milliliters?

   0.33 liter = ____ milliliters

5. **a.** Draw the level of the liquid in each cylinder to show the given amount.

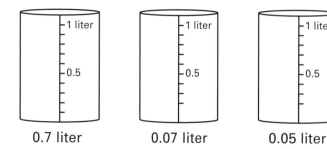
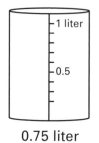
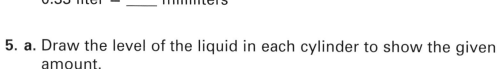

   0.7 liter   0.07 liter   0.05 liter   0.75 liter

   b. Order the amounts of liquid shown in part **a** from smallest to largest.

1. The water level is at the 0.1 liter mark. So the volume is one tenth of a liter.

2. You cannot measure 0.07 liter of liquid using this cylinder. Markings that show a hundredth of a liter would make it easier to measure 0.07 liter, but even then this would be difficult using this cylinder.

3.

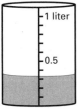

0.33 liters

4. a. 0.33 liter = 3.3 deciliters (dL)

 b. 0.33 liter = 33 centiliters (cL)

 c. 0.33 liter = 330 milliliters (mL)

5. a.

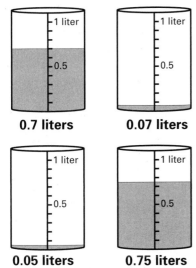

0.7 liters   0.07 liters

0.05 liters   0.75 liters

b. 0.05, 0.07, 0.7, 0.75

Students should notice that 0.7 is 10 times larger than 0.07. Also, 0.07 is very close to 0.05 but far from 0.7. Some students may notice that 0.75 is the same as 0.7 + 0.05.

Talk about how different amounts should be measured in different-sized cylinders.

The Meter

Around 1800, the meter was designed to be one ten-millionth of the distance between the Equator and the North Pole.

1. According to this design, how far is the North Pole from the Equator in meters? And in kilometers?

Several signs in Wisconsin and upper Michigan mark the halfway point between the Equator and the North Pole. There are two different ways to define halfway between the Equator and the North Pole. Here you see an example of each.

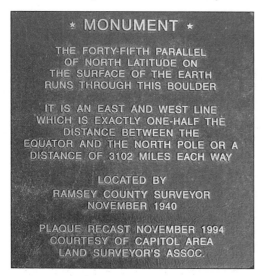

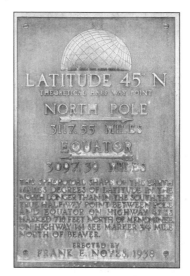

2. a. What are the two different ways to define halfway between the Equator and the North Pole?

b. Use the information on each sign to calculate the distance, in miles, from the North Pole to the Equator.

You have the distance between the Equator and the North Pole measured with two different units, a meter and a mile.

3. Use your answers to problems 1 and 2 to find two relationships between a meter and a mile.

Today, the meter is defined precisely; one mile is about 1609.344 meters.

4. Today, what is the precise distance from the equator to the North Pole? Calculate the distance in meters and in kilometers.

Mathematics in Context

1. The distance from the Equator to the North Pole was set at 10 million meters or 10,000 kilometers.

2. **a.** One way to define halfway is by equal distances to the North Pole and the Equator, like the sign on the left. The second way is using the 45th parallel of North latitude. Both signs give that information.

   b. There are two different distances.

   On the left: 6,204 miles = 3,102 × 2

   On the right: 6,214.94 miles = 3,117.55 + 3,097.39

3. 10,000,000 m = 6214.94 miles, equal distances from the North Pole to the Equator

   1609.026 m = 1 mile, dividing by 6,214.94 to get 1 mile relationship

4. 10,001,976 meters; this is about 10,002 kilometers.

   One mile is 1609.344 meters, so 6,214.94 miles is 6,214.94 × 1 mile and 6,214,94 × 1,609.344 meters ≈ 10,001,976 meters. Dividing by 1,000 m/km, this is about 10,002 kilometers.

Note: The Greek mathematician and philosopher Erathostenes already determined the circumference of our planet Earth by using the shadow of the sun.

How Fast? (page 1)

1. Marge drove 65 miles from Springfield to Boville. She left Springfield at 2:00 P.M. and arrived in Boville at 3:15 P.M. She uses this ratio table to find the average speed for her trip. Explain Marge's method.

Distance (in mi)	65	260	52
Time (in hours)	$1\frac{1}{4}$	5	1

2. Instead of writing $1\frac{1}{4}$ hours for the travel time, you can use quarters of an hour or minutes. Find the average speed for Marge's trip using the following ratio tables.

Distance (in mi)	65				
Time (in quarter hours)	5				

Distance (in mi)	65				
Time (in minutes)	75				

BOVILLE   65
MONTELLO   80
ST. CLARE   115

1. Sample explanation:

To change $1\frac{1}{4}$ hours to a whole number that is easier to work with, Marge multiplies the numbers of miles and hours by 4. Then she divides the numbers of miles and hours by 5 to find the number of miles traveled in one hour, which shows that she averages 52 miles per hour.

2. Sample ratio tables:

		÷ 5	× 4
Miles	65	13	52
Quarters of an Hour	5	1	4

		÷ 5	× 4
Miles	65	13	52
Hours	75	15	60

How Fast? (page 2)

3. Use a ratio table to calculate the average speed for each of the following trips.

   a. Departure Time: 8:00 A.M. Arrival Time: 9:30 A.M.
   Distance Traveled: 81 miles

Distance (in mi)						
Time (in)						

   b. Departure Time: 2:00 P.M. Arrival Time: 5:30 P.M.
   Distance Traveled: 140 miles

Distance (in mi)						
Time (in)						

   c. Departure Time: 8:15 A.M. Arrival Time: 10:00 A.M.
   Distance Traveled: 84 miles

Distance (in mi)						
Time (in)						

   d. Departure Time: 9:05 A.M. Arrival Time: 9:55 A.M.
   Distance Traveled: 30 miles

Distance (in mi)						
Time (in)						

   e. Departure Time: 7:30 A.M. Arrival Time: 4:00 P.M.
   Distance Traveled: 170 miles

Distance (in mi)						
Time (in)						

4. The average speed for the trip in part **e** above is very slow. Provide a possible explanation for the slow average speed.

Mathematics in Context

3. Sample responses:

a. 54 miles per hour

		×2	÷3
Distance (in mi)	81	162	54
Time (in hrs)	$1\frac{1}{2}$	3	1

b. 40 miles per hour

		×2	÷7
Distance (in mi)	140	280	40
Time (in hrs)	$3\frac{1}{2}$	7	1

c. 48 miles per hour

		÷7	×4
Distance (in mi)	84	12	48
Time (in quarters of an hour)	7	1	4

d. 36 miles per hour

		÷10	×12
Distance (in mi)	30	3	36
Time (in min)	50	5	60

e. 20 miles per hour

		×2	÷17
Distance (in mi)	170	340	20
Time (in hrs)	$8\frac{1}{2}$	17	1

4. Sample explanation:

The driver may have stopped for lunch or to take a break along the way.

Gas Mileage (page 1)

Mr. Van Dyke's science students are calculating the gas mileage of different cars. Gas mileage is the average number of miles that a car can travel on one gallon of gas.

1. Arnold is figuring out the gas mileage for a car that was driven 210 miles on 8.4 gallons of gas. He begins his calculations as shown here.

Distance (in mi)	210	2,100	300			
Gas (in gallons)	8.4	84				

a. Explain Arnold's first step.

b. Explain his next step.

c. Complete Arnold's calculations to find the car's gas mileage.

1. a. Sample explanation:

In Arnold's first step, he multiplied both the numbers of miles and gallons by 10 to change the decimal to a whole number.

b. In his next step, he tried to find the distance (in miles) per gallon. He starts by dividing by 7.

c. It is probably easier for Arnold to put in a few extra steps to make calculations easier. Sample ratio table:

	×10	÷7	÷3	÷4	
Distance (in mi)	210	2,100	300	100	25
Gas (in gallons)	8.4	84	12	4	1

Gas Mileage (page 2)

2. Using ratio tables, calculate the gas mileage for each of the following.

   a. A car travels 108 miles on 6 gallons of gasoline.

Distance (in mi)						
Gas (in gallons)						

   b. A car travels 252 miles on 12 gallons of gasoline.

Distance (in mi)						
Gas (in gallons)						

   c. A car travels 121 miles on 5.5 gallons of gasoline.

Distance (in mi)						
Gas (in gallons)						

   d. A car travels 164 miles on 8 gallons of gasoline.

Distance (in mi)						
Gas (in gallons)						

   e. A car travels 82.5 miles on 5.5 gallons of gasoline.

Distance (in mi)						
Gas (in gallons)						

3. If a car averages 20.5 miles per gallon of gas, how many gallons are needed to travel 492 miles? Use the following ratio table to calculate your answer.

Distance (in mi)						
Gas (in gallons)						

Mathematics in Context

2. a. 18 miles per gallon

		÷ 2	÷ 3	
Distance (in mi)	108	54	18	
Gas (in gallons)	6	3	1	

b. 21 miles per gallon

		÷ 2	÷ 3	÷ 2	
Distance (in mi)	252	126	42	21	
Gas (in gallons)	12	6	2	1	

c. 22 miles per gallon

		× 10	÷ 5	÷ 11	
Distance (in mi)	121	1,210	242	22	
Gas (in gallons)	5.5	55	11	1	

d. 20.5 miles per gallon

		÷ 2	÷ 4	
Distance (in mi)	164	82	20.5	
Gas (in gallons)	8	4	1	

e. 15 miles per gallon

		× 10	÷ 5	÷ 11	
Distance (in mi)	82.5	825	165	15	
Gas (in gallons)	5.5	55	11	1	

3. 24 gallons. Sample ratio table:

		× 2	× 10	÷ 5	× 6
Distance (in mi)	20.5	41	410	82	492
Gas (in gallons)	1	2	20	4	24

Gas Mileage Again (page 1)

Caroline's car averages 24 miles per gallon, which means that it needs 1 gallon of gas to travel 24 miles. Last year, Caroline drove her car 29,848 miles. She uses the following ratio table to calculate how many gallons of gas she used in her car during the year.

Distance (in mi)	24	24,000	4,800	960	29,760
Gas (in gallons)	1	1,000	200	40	1,240

Caroline concludes that she used a little more than 1,240 gallons of gas last year.

1. a. Explain Caroline's method.

b. Show another way to use a ratio table to calculate the number of gallons of gas Caroline used in her car last year.

1. a. Sample explanation:

First Caroline multiplies both the numbers of gallons and miles by 1,000. Then she multiplies the first column by 200. Next she multiplies the first column by 40. Finally, she adds the numbers in the previous three columns to get a total of 1,240 gallons for 29,760 miles.

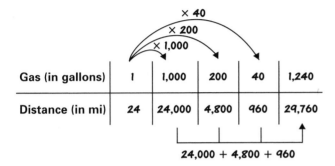

b. Sample ratio table:

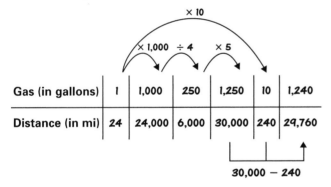

Note: Caroline's ratio table does not show the exact amount of gas used. Instead, she stops multiplying when she reaches a number that is close to the given number of miles (29,848). An even closer approximation for the number of gallons of gas that Caroline's car used is 1,244 gallons.

Gas Mileage Again (page 2)

2. For each of the following car trips, use a ratio table to find the approximate number of gallons of gas used. Then check your work with a calculator.

a. Mr. Sommers drove 195 miles, and his car averages 24 miles per gallon.

Distance (in mi)					
Gas (in gallons)					

b. Ms. Donno drove 316 miles, and her car averages 18 miles per gallon.

Distance (in mi)					
Gas (in gallons)					

c. Ms. Bartok drove 428 miles, and her car averages 23 miles per gallon.

Distance (in mi)					
Gas (in gallons)					

d. Mr. Aspen drove 391 miles, and his car averages 22 miles per gallon.

Distance (in mi)					
Gas (in gallons)					

e. Mr. Yuanes drove his car a total of 19,362 miles last year, and his car averages 21 miles per gallon.

Distance (in mi)					
Gas (in gallons)					

2. The ratio tables shown are sample tables, students' ratio tables may differ.

a. Approximately 8 gallons of gas were used.

	×2	×2	×2	
Distance (in mi)	24	48	96	192
Gas (in gallons)	1	2	4	8

b. Approximately 18 gallons of gas were used.

	×10	÷2	×3	÷5	
Distance (in mi)	18	180	90	270	54	324
Gas (in gallons)	1	10	5	15	3	18

270 + 54

c. Approximately 19 gallons of gas were used.

	×10	×2	
Distance (in mi)	23	230	460	437
Gas (in gallons)	1	10	20	19

460 − 23

d. Approximately 18 gallons of gas were used.

	×10	÷2	×3	÷5	
Distance (in mi)	22	220	110	330	66	396
Gas (in gallons)	1	10	5	15	3	18

330 + 66

e. Exactly 922 gallons of gas were used.

		×9	×100		×10	
Distance (in mi)	21	189	18,900	42	420	19,362
Gas (in gallons)	1	9	900	2	20	922

18,900 + 42 + 420

Population (page 1)

1. In Sun City, there is one horse for every five people. What is the horse to people ratio for Moon City? You may want to use a ratio table for your calculations.

2. In Dustown, there are 28 horses per 100 inhabitants.

   a. Which town has the least number of horses relative to its population—Sun City, Moon City, or Dustown?

   b. The population of Dustown is 1,368. How many horses are there in the town?

1. In Moon City, there are six horses per person.
(720 horses: 120 people or 6:1).

	÷ 10	÷ 6	÷ 2	
Horses	720	72	12	6
People	120	12	2	1

2. a. Sun City has relatively the smallest number
of horses.

Sun City: 1 horse per 5 people or 20 horses
per 100 inhabitants.

Dustown: 28 horses per 100 inhabitants

Moon City: 6 horses per 1 person or 600
horses per 100 inhabitants.

b. There are approximately 385 horses in
Dustown. Sample strategies:

Strategy 1

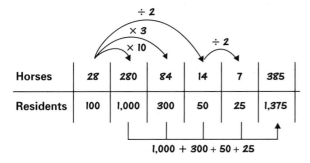

| | ÷ 2 | | | ÷ 2 | | |
| | × 3 | | | | | |
	× 10					
Horses	28	280	84	14	7	385
Residents	100	1,000	300	50	25	1,375

1,000 + 300 + 50 + 25

Strategy 2

Since there are 28 horses for every 100
inhabitants, each inhabitant has 0.28 of a
horse. So 1,368 inhabitants have 1,368 × 0.28
horses, or 383 horses.

Population (page 2)

3. Summarize the following information as a ratio
(_____ per 100).

   a. Switzerland has approximately 7,404,055 inhabitants
and 3,940,000 television sets.

   b. Taiwan has approximately 22,647,000 inhabitants
and 13,355,000 telephones.

   c. Greece has approximately 11,000,000 inhabitants
and 5,220,000 radios.

   d. Japan has approximately 127.5 million inhabitants.
Each day, approximately 73,300,000 newspapers
are sold.

   e. Jamaica has approximately 2,644,000 inhabitants
and 168,179 passenger cars.

Answers will vary, depending on how students choose to display their ratios. For each problem a sample response is given below.

3. a. About 1 television set per 2 inhabitants, or 50 television sets per 100 inhabitants.

Inhabitants	7,404,055	2	200	100
Television Sets	3,940000	1	100	50

Note: Some students might find the number of inhabitants per 100 televisions. Discuss the meaning of this ratio.

b. About 1 telephone per 1.5 inhabitants, or 67 telephones per 100 inhabitants.

Inhabitants	22,647,000	1.5	150	50	100
Telephones	13,355,000	1	100	33.3	67

Note: Make sure students realize that these are approximations. Discuss why this is appropriate.

c. About 1 radio per 2 inhabitants, or 50 radios per 100 inhabitants.

Inhabitants	11,000,000	2	100
Radios	5,220,000	1	50

d. About 1.7 inhabitants per newspaper, or 60 newspapers per 100 inhabitants.

Inhabitants	127,500,000	1.7	17	100
Newspapers	73,300,000	1	10	60

e. About 1 car per 15.7 inhabitants, or about 6 cars per 100 inhabitants.

Inhabitants	2,644,000	15.7	157	50	100
Passenger Cars	168,179	1	10	3	6

Note: Discuss with students why the answers are estimates and not exact ratios.

Car (page 1)

The table shows the number of passenger cars and the population in several countries.

Country	Number of Passenger Cars	Population
Italy	31,953,247	57,816,000
Japan	42,655,000	127,635,000
Seychelles	6,970	80,000
United States	133,621,000	293,633,000
Democratic Republic of Congo	787,000	58,318,000

1. a. Which country has the most passenger cars?

b. Which country has the most passenger cars relative to its population? Explain.

When comparing ratios, such as the ones above, it is helpful to organize your data in a ratio table. You can round numbers in ratio tables, as shown below.

Italy

Number of Passenger Cars	32			
Popluation	58			

United States

Number of Passenger Cars	134			
Popluation	294			

2. a. Explain what is shown in the two ratio tables above.

b. How can you determine which country has more cars relative to its population, using the two ratio tables above?

Mathematics in Context

1. a. The United States has the most passenger cars.

b. Italy has the most passenger cars relative to its population. Sample explanation:

After estimating the ratio of cars to people for each country, I decided that either the United States or Italy has the most passenger cars relative to its population. Because Italy has more than 1 car per 2 people (32 cars per 58 people) and the United States has less than 1 car per 2 people (134 cars per 294 people),Italy has the most cars relative to its population.

2. a. The numbers in the ratio tables show the numbers of passenger cars and people for Italy and the United States, rounded to the nearest million.

b. Sample explanation:

By filling in the ratio tables as shown below, I can determine that Italy has more than 1 car per 2 people, whereas the United States has less than 1 car per 2 people.

Italy

Number of Passenger Cars	32	16	
Population	58	29	

United States

Number of Passenger Cars	134	72	6	
Population	294	132	11	

Car (page 2)

Country	Number of Passenger Cars	Population
Italy	31,953,247	57,816,000
Japan	42,655,000	127,635,000
Seychelles	6,970	80,000
United States	133,621,000	293,633,000
Democratic Republic of Congo	787,000	58,318,000

3. Order the five countries according to the number of cars relative to population.

   _____

   _____

   _____

   _____

   _____

4. You can express the relative number of cars in a country as the number of cars per 100 people. In Italy, for example, there are approximately 31.9 million passenger cars and 57.8 million people. This translates to 55 cars per 100 people.

   a. Use a calculator to find the number of cars per 100 people for the five countries.

   b. Explain why it is easier to compare "cars per 100 people" than "cars per person" or "cars per 10,000 people" in part a above.

Mathematics in Context

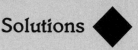
3. Italy, United States, Japan, Seychelles, and Democratic Republic of Congo. Sample strategy:

The answer to problem 2 on the previous page shows that Italy has the most passenger cars and the United States the second most, so you only need to compare the remaining countries, Japan, Seychelles, and Democratic Republic of Congo. Here are ratio table strategies to compare the remaining countries.

Japan

Number of Passenger Cars	42	21
Population	128	64

Seychelles

Number of Passenger Cars	7	21
Population	80	240

Democratic Republic of Congo

Number of Passenger Cars	800	8	4	20
Population	58,300	583	292	1,460

Students may round the last ratio table entry to 50 passenger cars for Japan and Seychelles in order to compare the countries.

4. a. Italy: 55 per 100

Japan: 33 per 100

Seychelles: 9 per 100

United States: 45 per 100

Democratic Republic of Congo: 1.3 per 100

Using a calculator, divide the number of cars by the population to find each ratio and then multiply by 100.

b. Sample explanation:

For these five countries, "cars per person" is always a decimal number, and "cars per 10,000 people" results in a very precise number. "Cars per 100 people" results in a whole number (except for Democratic Republic of Congo). Since whole numbers are easy to work with, it is preferable to use "cars per 100 people."

What Fractions?

The middle school in Woolton has 391 students. Fifty-one of the students are from a small town nearby, named Ridgeway. The principal claims, "One-eighth of our students are from Ridgeway."

1. Do you agree with the principal? Why or why not?

People sometimes round figures because precise amounts are not important in particular situations. Rounded figures are often better because they are easier to interpret and work with. Instead of saying "293 out of 391 students," for example, you can say "three-fourths of the students."

2. Use an easy-to-work-with fraction to describe each situation.

a. Six hundred fifteen readers have returned an opinion poll from *Radio Week* magazine. Three hundred ninety-seven say that WOLX is their favorite radio station.

b. Of those 615 respondents, 125 like listening to country music.

c. Fifty-nine of the 615 respondents regularly go to the movies.

d. The population of Albertville is 54,273,372. Of the people in Albertville, 9,012,461 are children under the age of 10.

e. In Dunhill, 9,321,989 people are under the age of 60.
The population of Dunhill is 11,953,521.

f. The school library has 937 books, of which 240 are fiction.

g. There are 83 houses in Pilton, 63 of which are painted white.

h. Yesterday, Sondra counted her baseball cards and found that she had 78 of them. After giving some to a friend, she has 61 cards.

i. Juan had 52 baseball cards. After buying some more, he has a total of 75 cards.

1. Yes, the principal is correct because 51 out of 391 is about 50 out of 400, which is $\frac{1}{8}$.

2. Answers will vary because students will round differently, but all answers should be benchmark fractions. Accept any answer that is reasonable. Sample responses:

a. 397 out of 615 is about 400 out of 600, or $\frac{2}{3}$.

b. 125 out of 615 is about 125 out of 625, or about $\frac{1}{5}$.

c. 59 out of 615 is about 60 out of 600, or $\frac{1}{10}$.

d. 9,012,461 out of 54,273,372 is about 9 out of 54, or $\frac{1}{6}$.

e. 9,321,989 out of 11,953,521 is about 9 out of 12, or $\frac{3}{4}$.

f. 240 out of 937 is about 250 out of 1,000, or $\frac{1}{4}$.

g. 63 out of 83 is about 60 out of 80, or $\frac{3}{4}$.

h. 61 out of 78 is about 60 out of 80, or $\frac{3}{4}$.

i. 75 out of 52 is about 75 out of 50, or $\frac{3}{2}$.

Extension

Ask students whether the benchmark fraction is greater than or less than the original ratio.

Name _____ Date_____ Class_____

Watermelons (page 1)

Keith grows watermelons in his garden and then sells them for $1.80 per kilogram (kg). Watermelons usually do not weigh exactly one or two kilograms, so Keith uses a double number line to find the price of each one.

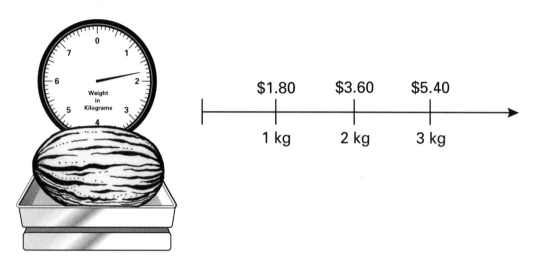

1. Explain how Keith finds the price of a watermelon weighing $1\frac{3}{4}$ kg by using the double number line.

2. Use a double number line to find the prices of watermelons that weigh the following amounts.

   a. $\frac{3}{4}$ kg

   b. $1\frac{1}{3}$ kg

   c. $2\frac{2}{3}$ kg

   d. $1\frac{1}{4}$ kg

   e. $1\frac{1}{2}$ kg

1. $1\frac{3}{4}$ kilograms cost \$3.15. Sample explanation using a double number line:

One kilogram of watermelon costs \$1.80, so $\frac{1}{2}$ kg is \$0.90, and $\frac{1}{4}$ kg is \$0.45. So $1\frac{3}{4}$ kg is the sum of 1 kg, $\frac{1}{2}$ kg, and $\frac{1}{4}$ kg, for a cost of \$3.15 (\$1.80 + \$0.90 + \$0.45).

Note: Many students like to partition the first interval and use that as a base. Others might prefer to label partitions between whole number amounts. Both strategies are shown below.

2. a. \$1.35 (\$0.90 + \$0.45)

  b. \$2.40 (\$1.80 + \$0.60)

  c. \$4.80 (\$3.60 + \$1.20)

  d. \$2.25 (\$1.80 + \$0.45)

  e. \$2.70 (\$1.80 + \$0.90)

For parts **a, d**, and **e**, students can use the following double number line.

For parts **b** and **c**, students can use the following double number line.

Watermelons (page 2)

3. Keith lowers his price for watermelons to $1.20 per kilogram.
Revise the watermelon prices to reflect the sale price.

a. $\frac{3}{4}$ kg

b. $1\frac{1}{3}$ kg

c. $2\frac{2}{3}$ kg

d. $1\frac{1}{4}$ kg

e. $1\frac{1}{2}$ kg

If you have to calculate $\frac{1}{2} \times 1.20$, you can think of the problem:
What will $\frac{1}{2}$ kg of watermelons cost, priced at $1.20 per kilogram?
Calculating $\frac{1}{2} \times 1.20$ is the same as calculating $\frac{1}{2}$ of 1.20.

4. Complete each of the following calculations. Show your work.

a. $1\frac{1}{3} \times 1.80$

b. $2\frac{3}{4} \times 1.60$

c. $1\frac{2}{3} \times 3.60$

d. $\frac{3}{4}$ of 0.80

e. $2\frac{1}{4}$ of 0.40

3. a. $0.90 ($0.60 + $0.30)

 b. $1.60 ($1.20 + $0.40)

 c. $3.20 ($2.40 + $0.80)

 d. $1.50 ($1.20 + $0.30)

 e. $1.80 ($1.20 + $0.60)

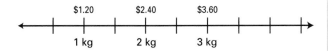

4. a. 2.4

Using a double number line:

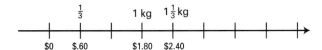

Using a ratio table:

Weight (in kg)	1	$\frac{1}{3}$	$1\frac{1}{3}$
Price (in dollars)	1.80	0.60	2.40

 b. 4.4 I thought of kilogram of watermelon costs $1.60, so $\frac{1}{4}$ kg is $0.40, and $\frac{3}{4}$ kg is $1.20 (3 × $0.40). $2\frac{3}{4}$ kg is the sum of 2 kg and $\frac{3}{4}$ kg, for a cost of $4.40 ($3.20 + $1.20).

 c. 6 I thought of $1\frac{2}{3}$ kg of watermelons, priced at $3.60 per kilogram. $\frac{1}{3}$ kg is $1.20, so $\frac{2}{3}$ kg is $2.40 (2 × $1.20), and $1\frac{2}{3}$ kg is $6.00 ($3.60 + $2.40).

 d. 0.6 I thought of $\frac{3}{4}$ kg of watermelons, priced at $0.80 per kilogram. $\frac{1}{4}$ of $0.80 is $0.20, so $\frac{3}{4}$ of $0.80 is $0.60 (3 × $0.20).

 e. 0.9 I thought of $2\frac{1}{4}$ kg of watermelons, priced at $0.40 per kilogram. $\frac{1}{4}$ of $0.40 is $0.10 and 2 of $0.40 is $0.80, so $2\frac{1}{4}$ of $0.40 is $0.90 ($0.80 + $0.10).

Note: Discuss with students how it often helps when doing a "bare" calculation, to think of a situation they have seen earlier. You might discuss why it is not important to write the trailing zeros in the answers.

Name _____ Date_____ Class_____

At the Market (page 1)

Jim runs a produce stand at the market. Jim is too busy at the stand to use a calculator, so he has become very good at calculating prices mentally. To make calculations easier, he rounds the amounts shown on the scale to the nearest benchmark fraction.

1. If one kilogram of grapes costs $1.60, find the prices that Jim will charge for the following amounts of grapes.

a.

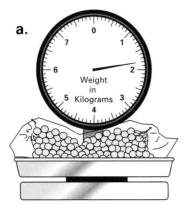

b.

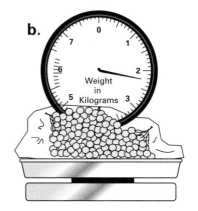

c.

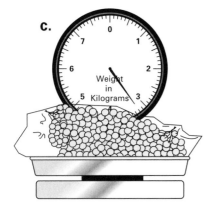

d.

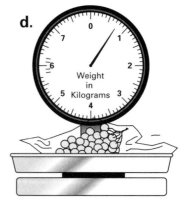

1. Answers will vary. Accept answers that are reasonably close to the following:

   a. $2.80 ($1\frac{3}{4}$ kilograms)

   b. $3.60 ($2\frac{1}{4}$ kilograms)

   c. $5.20 ($3\frac{1}{4}$ kilograms)

   d. $1.20 ($\frac{3}{4}$ kilograms)

   Students can round the amounts shown on the scales to the nearest quarter kilogram and then use a double number line, as shown below, to find their answers.

At the Market (page 2)

2. One day Jim's scale breaks down, so he borrows a digital scale that shows the weight of items in very precise decimal notation. For the first four items that Jim sells, the scale indicates the following weights: 2.212, 0.760, 1.461, and 2.110. Explain why the decimal scale might be more difficult for Jim to use.

3. Jim decides to convert the weights shown on the decimal scale to the nearest benchmark fraction. For example, if the scale shows 1.739, Jim converts this decimal to $1\frac{3}{4}$. Convert each of the following decimals to fractions that will be easy for Jim to work with mentally.

   a. 2.772 kg

   b. 3.236 kg

   c. 1.401 kg

   d. 2.352 kg

   e. 2.534 kg

   f. 1.690 kg

   g. 2.110 kg

   h. 3.728 kg

   i. 0.317 kg

   j. 2.289 kg

2. Explanations will vary. Sample explanation:

Since the decimals are very precise, each one contains a lot of digits, making it difficult to multiply mentally.

3. Answers may vary, depending on how students round each decimal. All answers should be benchmark fractions. Sample responses:

a. $2\frac{3}{4}$

b. $3\frac{1}{4}$

c. $1\frac{1}{3}$, $1\frac{2}{5}$, or $1\frac{1}{2}$

d. $2\frac{1}{3}$

e. $2\frac{1}{2}$

f. $1\frac{2}{3}$

g. $2\frac{1}{10}$

h. $3\frac{3}{4}$

i. $\frac{1}{3}$

j. $2\frac{1}{4}$ or $2\frac{1}{3}$

At the Market (page 3)

4. Find the price that Jim will charge for each of the following by first converting the decimal to a benchmark fraction and then using a mental calculation or a double number line strategy.

a. 1.327 kg of white grapes at $2.10 per kilogram

b. 3.532 kg of apples at $1.10 per kilogram

c. 0.728 kg of oranges at $4.00 per kilogram

d. 0.229 kg of potatoes at $0.80 per kilogram

e. 3.996 kg of watermelon at $1.80 per kilogram

4. Answers may vary, depending on how students convert the decimals to fractions. Accept all reasonable answers.

a. $1\frac{1}{3} \times \$2.10 = \$2.80$

Students can round 1.327 to $1\frac{1}{3}$ and then use a double number line.

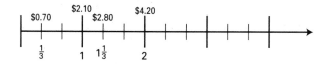

b. $3\frac{1}{2} \times \$1.10 = \$3.85$

Students can round 3.532 to $3\frac{1}{2}$ and then use a double number line.

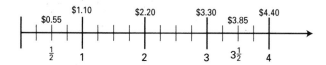

c. $\frac{3}{4} \times \$4.00 = \$3.00$

Students can round 0.728 to $\frac{3}{4}$ and then use a double number line.

d. $\frac{1}{4} \times \$0.80 = \$0.20$

Students can round 0.229 to $\frac{1}{4}$ and then use a double number line.

e. $4 \times \$1.80 = \$7.20$

Students can round 3.996 to 4 and then use a double number line.

Fraction of a Fraction

1. One-half of the students in Ms. Abel's class are girls, and $\frac{1}{3}$ of the girls have brown hair. If there are four girls in the class who have brown hair, how many students are there in Ms. Abel's class?

2. One-third of the students in Mr. Tolme's class are boys, and $\frac{1}{2}$ of the boys play a musical instrument. How many boys in Mr. Tolme's class play a musical instrument? Note that many answers are possible.

3. One-fourth of the students at Milton Middle School get a ride to school. One-half of these students ride with their parents. What fraction of the students ride with their parents?

4. Find the answer to each of the following.

   a. $\frac{1}{2}$ of $\frac{1}{4}$ mile

   b. $\frac{1}{3}$ of $\frac{1}{2}$ an hour

   c. $\frac{1}{2}$ of $\frac{1}{3}$ an hour

   d. $\frac{1}{3}$ of $\frac{1}{3}$ liter

   e. $\frac{1}{2}$ of $\frac{1}{5}$ kilometer

   f. $\frac{1}{4}$ of $\frac{1}{3}$ meter

   g. $\frac{1}{3}$ of $\frac{3}{4}$ kilogram

   h. $\frac{1}{2}$ of $\frac{2}{3}$ of the boys

   i. $\frac{3}{4}$ of $\frac{1}{2}$ cup

   j. $\frac{2}{3}$ of $\frac{2}{3}$ of the girls

1. There are 24 students in the class. Sample strategy:

Since four girls have brown hair and $\frac{1}{3}$ of the girls have brown hair, there are 12 girls in the class ($\frac{3}{3}$ is 3 groups of 4). Since half of the students are girls, there are 24 students in the class (2 groups of 12).

Some student might draw a bar model:

brown
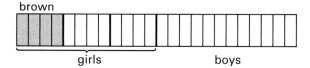

girls   boys

2. Many answers are possible for the number of boys that play an instrument. The total number of students in class must be a multiple of six. Here is the beginning of all possible responses.

Total Students	Boys	Boys Playing an Instrument
6	2	1
12	4	2
18	6	3
24	8	4

3. One-eighth of the students get a ride from their parents. Sample strategies:

Strategy 1

If I have a bar with 16 segments, $\frac{1}{4}$ of the segments is 4, and $\frac{1}{2}$ of 4 is 2. Two out of 16 is the same as 1 out of 8, which is $\frac{1}{8}$.

Strategy 2

If you want to find one-fourth of something, you take half of it and then take half again. Half of $\frac{1}{2}$ is $\frac{1}{4}$; $\frac{1}{2}$ of $\frac{1}{4}$ is $\frac{1}{8}$.

4. **a.** $\frac{1}{8}$ mile   **f.** $\frac{1}{12}$ meter

   b. $\frac{1}{6}$ hour   **g.** $\frac{3}{12}$ or $\frac{1}{4}$ kilogram

   c. $\frac{1}{6}$ hour   **h.** $\frac{2}{6}$ or $\frac{1}{3}$ of the boys

   d. $\frac{1}{9}$ liter   **i.** $\frac{3}{8}$ cup

   e. $\frac{1}{10}$ kilometer   **j.** $\frac{4}{9}$ of the girls

Note: If students have trouble, suggest that they make up a problem like the ones above. You might discuss any patterns they notice in their final answers. You might suggest that they draw a bar model.

The Deli

Amy is buying some meat and cheese at the deli. Swiss cheese costs $3.60 per pound (lb), but Amy needs only 0.75 lb. She uses the following arrow string to compute how much 0.75 lb of Swiss cheese will cost.

$$\$3.60 \xrightarrow{\div 4} \$0.90 \xrightarrow{\times 3} \$2.70$$

1. Explain Amy's method.

2. Solve Amy's problem using a ratio table.

3. Find the prices for these purchases at the deli. Show how you found each price.

a. Ham costs $3.20 per pound. How much does 0.75 lb cost?

b. Cheddar cheese costs $7.50 per pound. How much does 0.80 lb cost?

c. Salami costs $4.00 per pound. How much does 0.40 lb cost?

d. Bologna costs $3.00 per pound. How much does 0.60 lb cost?

e. Pepperoni costs $2.40 per pound. How much does 1.25 lb cost?

f. Carol pays $1.80 for 0.75 lb of American cheese. What is the price per pound of American cheese?

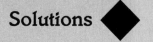
1. Explanations will vary. Sample explanation:

   Since 0.75 is the same as $\frac{3}{4}$, Amy multiplies the price per pound of Swiss cheese by $\frac{3}{4}$. She does this multiplication in two steps with an arrow string that first divides by 4 and then multiplies by 3.

2. Different ratio tables are possible.

   When she divides by 4 she knows how much $\frac{1}{4}$ lb costs; when she multiplies by 3 she knows how much $\frac{3}{4}$ lb costs.

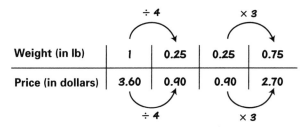

Weight (in lb)	1	0.25	0.25	0.75
Price (in dollars)	3.60	0.90	0.90	2.70

3. Students may use their own strategy. A strategy using arrow language is shown for each problem.

   a. 0.75 pound of ham costs $2.40
   $3.20 $\xrightarrow{\div 4}$ $0.80 $\xrightarrow{\times 3}$ $2.40

   b. 0.8 pound of cheddar costs $6
   $7.50 $\xrightarrow{\div 10}$ $0.75 $\xrightarrow{\times 8}$ $6.00

   c. 0.4 pound of salami costs $1.60
   $4.00 $\xrightarrow{\div 10}$ $0.40 $\xrightarrow{\times 4}$ $1.60

   d. 0.6 pound of bologna costs $1.80
   $3.00 $\xrightarrow{\div 10}$ $0.30 $\xrightarrow{\times 6}$ $1.80

   e. 1.25 pounds of pepperoni cost $3
   $2.40 $\xrightarrow{\div 4}$ $0.60 $\xrightarrow{\times 5}$ $3.00

   f. The price per pound of American cheese is $2.40. Students may use reverse arrow strings to solve part **f**, as shown:

   $2.40 $\xleftarrow{\times 4}$ $0.60 $\xleftarrow{\div 3}$ $1.80

Percents (page 1)

To celebrate spring, Teri's Boutique is having its annual *Temperature Sale!*

The sale price depends on the current temperature outside. Today, the current temperature is 85°F, so the sale price of any item in the store is 85% of the regular price.

Anwar wants to buy a jacket, regularly priced at $140. What is the sale price?

Anwar uses a percent bar to begin his calculation.

140 Price (in dollars)

0% 5% 10%   85%   100%

1. Finish Anwar's strategy to calculate the sale price of the jacket.

Sondra wants to buy a sweater, regularly priced at $55. What is the sale price?

Sondra uses a ratio table to begin her calculation.

Price (in dollars)	55	5.5			
Percentage	100	10			

2. Finish Sondra's strategy to calculate the sale price of the sweater.

3. Use a ratio table to find the sale price for each of the following.

Temperature Sale!		
Regular Price	**Current Temperature**	**Sale Price**
a. $24	75°F	
b. $80	64°F	
c. $90	72°F	

1. The sale price is $119. Here is what Anwar's strategy may have been:

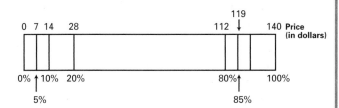

2. The sale price of the sweater is $46.75. Here is what Sondra's strategy may have been:

Price (in dollars)	55	5.5	2.75	11	22	44	46.75
Percentage	100	10	5	20	40	80	85

3. Note that students should choose the strategy they feel comfortable with. You may want to discuss students' strategies after finishing problem 3.

a. $18

Price (in dollars)	24	12	6	18
Percentage	100	50	25	75

b. $51.20

$$40 + 8 + 3.20$$

Price (in dollars)	80	40	8	0.80	3.20	51.20
Percentage	100	50	10	1	4	64

c. $64.80

$$45 + 1.80 + 18$$

Price (in dollars)	90	45	9	0.90	1.80	18	64.80
Percentage	100	50	10	1	2	20	72

Percents (page 2)

Solve the following problems. Show your strategy.

On Wednesday, the temperature was 60°F .

4. a. Julius bought a pair of shoes for $48.
   What was the original price?

b. Samantha bought a blouse for $12.
   What was the original price?

Two weeks later, Tim bought a pair of shorts for $22. The original price was $55.

5. What was the temperature that day?

There are three main types of percentage problems.

   i. Calculate the part.

   ii. Calculate the total.

   iii. Calculate the percent.

6. For the following percent bars, identify which type of problem (**i, ii,** or **iii**) is involved. Then calculate the missing numbers.

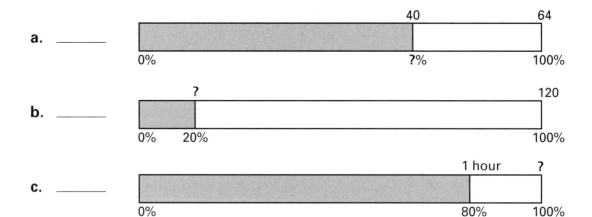

a. _____

b. _____

c. _____

4. Note that students may choose their own strategy. For each problem one sample strategy is shown.

a. The original price of the shoes was $80. Sample strategy, using a percent bar:

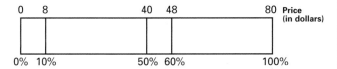

Sample explanation: First I made a whole percentage bar showing 100%, which represents the original price. Then I placed a vertical line at $\frac{6}{10}$ of the bar, showing 60% of the original price or $48, which was the sale price. I divided this percentage by six to get 10% of the original price or $8 and multiplied by five to find $40, which is 50% of the original price. Then I knew the original price had to be 2 × $40 = $80.

b. The original price of the blouse was $20. Sample strategy, using a ratio table:

Price (in dollars)	12	2	20
Percentage	60	10	100

5. The temperature was 40°F. The table below shows the percentage was 40%.

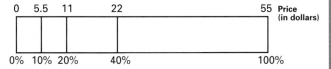

Sample explanation: First I made a whole percentage bar showing a price of $55 at 100%, which was the original price. Then I placed a vertical line at $\frac{1}{10}$ of the bar, showing 10% of the original price or $5.5. I doubled this percentage to get 20% of the original price or $11 and doubled again to find $22, which is 40% of the original price.

6. a. Calculate the percent. 100% ÷ 8 = 12.5%; 5 × 12.5% = 62.5%

Price (in dollars)	64	8	40
Percentage	100	12.5	62.5

b. Calculate the part. 10% of $120 is $12, 20% of $120 is 2 × $12 = $24

c. Calculate the total. 80% represents 1 hour, or 60 minutes.

20% represents $\frac{1}{4}$ × 60 min = 15 minutes

100% represents 5 × 15 min = 75 minutes or 1 hour and 15 minutes.

Name _____ Date_____ Class_____

Area Model (page 1)

Here is a scaled drawing of a beautiful square
terrace. Each tile is imported from Italy and
measures 1 m by 1 m.

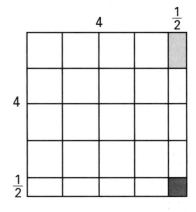

1. a. A small part of a tile is colored light gray.
What fractional part of a tile is this piece?

  b. And the part in the bottom right corner?

  c. Use this drawing to calculate the area of
the whole terrace.

2. A smaller square terrace has side lengths of $3\frac{1}{2}$ m.
Calculate the area of this terrace. Show your work.

3. a. On the drawing, label the
area of each of the parts.

  b. What is $(7\frac{1}{2})^2 = ?$

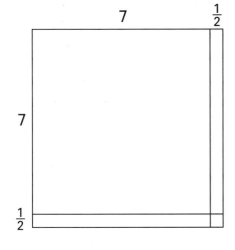

4. a. On the drawing, label the
area of each of the parts.

  b. What is $(6\frac{1}{3})^2 = ?$

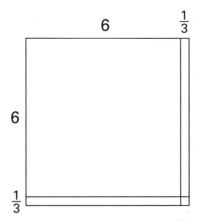

1. a. The shaded partial tile is $\frac{1}{2}$ a tile, using one square tile as a measuring unit.

b. The dark part in the bottom right corner is $\frac{1}{4}$ of a tile.

c. $20\frac{1}{4}$

There are 16 (4 × 4) whole tiles.

There are eight $\frac{1}{2}$ tiles ($4 \times \frac{1}{2} + 4 \times \frac{1}{2}$).

There is one quarter of a tile in the lower right-hand corner.

The area of the terrace is $20\frac{1}{4}$, the sum of the parts ($16 + 2 + 2 + \frac{1}{4}$).

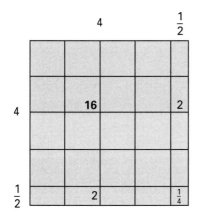

2. The area is $12\frac{1}{4}$ m^2

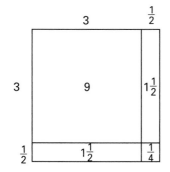

3. a.

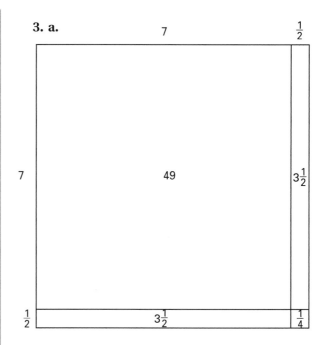

b. $(7\frac{1}{2})^2 = 56\frac{1}{4}$ ($49 + 3\frac{1}{2} + 3\frac{1}{2} + \frac{1}{4}$)

4. a.

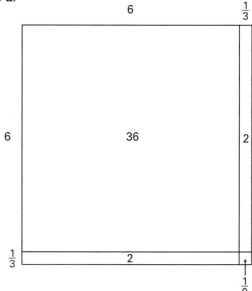

b. $(6\frac{1}{3})^2 = 40\frac{1}{9}$ ($36 + 2 + 2 + \frac{1}{9}$)

Area Model (page 2)

5. Write the multiplication problem represented by this rectangle.

	?	?
?	12	1
?	3	$\frac{1}{4}$

6. Write the problem represented by this square.

?	0.75
0.75	0.25

7. Make up your own area model problem. Ask a classmate to solve your problem.

5. $6\frac{1}{2} \times 2\frac{1}{2} = 16\frac{1}{4}$ Sample reasoning:

First I considered dimensions of the largest rectangle; they need to be factors of 12. Then I considered the next largest rectangle; it would help if the longest side was also divisible by 3. I tried 6 × 2, and it seems to work. Back to the smaller rectangle, 6 × ? = 3, so the shorter side has a length of $\frac{1}{2}$.

Then I considered the smallest rectangle $\frac{1}{2} \times$? $= \frac{1}{4}$. So the unknown length is one-half. This makes the dimensions of the last rectangle 2 by $\frac{1}{2}$, which checks with the area of 1.

6. This is a 2 by 2 square, with an area of 4 square units. A multiplication problem is (1.5 + 0.5) × (1.5 + 0.5). The area of the missing rectangle is 2.25 square units.

Sample reasoning:

First I considered the smallest square with an area of 0.25 squares. The side length is 0.5. Then I considered the rectangle with an area of 0.75; 0.5 × ? = 0.75 or half of some number is three-fourths. It must be 1.5.

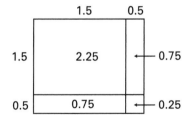

7. Have students discuss their answers with a classmate. You may want to share some of their problems with the whole class.

Scale (page 1)

To find the area of a space, it is important to write the dimension as a single unit, using either fractions or decimals.
For example, 7' 6" is $7\frac{1}{2}$' or 7.5'.

1. Write the dimensions of each room as a single unit.

a. Bedroom 10' 3" × 16' 6" _____

b. Family Room 16' 9" × 15' 4" _____

Here you see a drawing of the bedroom. Note that this drawing is not to scale.

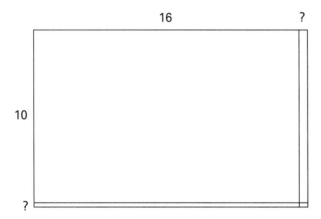

2. Fill in the missing numbers and calculate the area of the bedroom in square feet.

A common scale for working with floor plans is 1":48". So one inch in the drawing is 48 inches in reality.

3. Use the scale line to find the actual dimensions of this bathroom using inches.

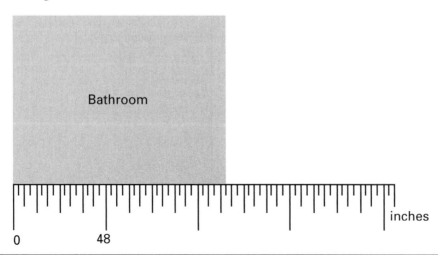

1. a. $10\frac{1}{4}' \times 16\frac{1}{2}'$ or $10.25' \times 16.5'$

  b. $16\frac{3}{4}' \times 15\frac{1}{3}'$ or 16.75×15.33

2. Note that students may choose to use fractions or decimals. In this sample explanation, fractions are used.

The question marks represent $\frac{1}{2}$ on the horizontal line and $\frac{1}{4}$ on the vertical line ($10\frac{1}{4}' \times 16\frac{1}{2}'$ or $10.25' \times 16.5'$).

The missing numbers are $10 \times 16 = 160$;

$10 \times \frac{1}{2} = 5$

$\frac{1}{4} \times 16 = 4$

$\frac{1}{4} \times \frac{1}{2} = \frac{1}{8}$

The area of the bedroom floor is $160 + 5 + 4 + \frac{1}{8} = 169\frac{1}{8}$ square feet.

3. Dimensions of the bathroom: length $111''$ and width $84''$

					Length	Width				
Floor Plan (in inches)	1	2	$\frac{1}{16}$	$\frac{5}{16}$	$2\frac{5}{16}$	$\frac{1}{16}$	$\frac{10}{16}$	$\frac{2}{16}$	$\frac{12}{16}$	$1\frac{12}{16}$
Actual Dimension (in inches)	48	96	3	15	111	3	30	6	36	84

Scale (page 2)

The scale 1":48" is often written as 1":4', and called a *quarter-inch scale*.

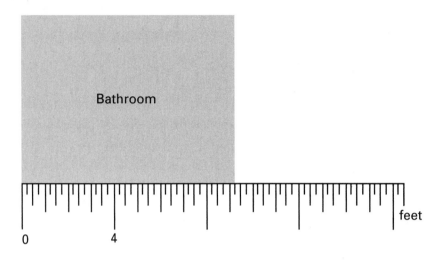

4. **a.** Use this scale line to find the actual dimensions of the bathroom using feet.

   b. How can you use both scale lines to find the dimensions of the bathroom using a whole number of feet and inches?

5. Make a scale drawing of the two rooms in problem 1 on a quarter-inch scale.

4. a. Dimensions of the bathroom: length $9\frac{1}{4}'$ and width $7'$

					Length			Width		
Floor Plan (in inches)	1	2	$\frac{1}{16}$	$\frac{5}{16}$	$2\frac{5}{16}$	$\frac{1}{16}$	$\frac{10}{16}$	$\frac{2}{16}$	$\frac{12}{16}$	$1\frac{12}{16}$
Actual Dimension (in ft)	4	8	$\frac{1}{4}$	$1\frac{1}{4}$	$9\frac{1}{4}$	$\frac{1}{4}$	$\frac{10}{4}$	$\frac{2}{4}$	$\frac{12}{4}$	7

b. Sample answer: You could use the scale marked in feet to find the nearest whole foot. Then you could use the scale marked in inches and check how much extra over a whole foot is left. Every four marks on the scale in inches is one foot. So the first three marks after the whole foot mark are 3, 6, and 9 inches.

5. Check the dimensions of students' drawings and check for neatness of drawings. Students should use an inch-ruler to make correct drawings.

The dimensions of the scale drawings are:

Bedroom $2\frac{9}{16}'' \times 4\frac{1}{8}''$

Family Room $4\frac{3}{16}'' \times 3\frac{5}{6}''$

Name _____ **Date** _____ **Class** _____

The Bus Company

A bus company requested two proposals for placing bus stops along a six-mile bus route.

Proposal I has stops every $\frac{3}{4}$ of a mile.

1 mile

Town A   Town B

1. a. How many stops will there be?

   b. Use the scale line to help you accurately mark all of the proposed bus stops on the number line route above.

Proposal II has stops every $\frac{3}{8}$ of a mile.

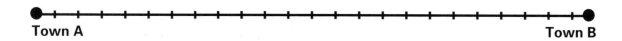

Town A   Town B

2. a. How many stops will there be?

   b. Use the scale line to help you accurately mark all of the proposed bus stops on the number line route above.

3. Show both proposals by filling in this ratio table. Start with the ones that are the easiest to calculate! Whenever possible, simplify your answers. Two answers have been done for you.

Stop Number	1	2	3	4	5	6	7	8	9	10
Proposal I Distance (in mi)	$\frac{3}{4}$	$1\frac{1}{2}$	$2\frac{1}{4}$							
Proposal II Distance (in mi)	$\frac{3}{8}$									

1. a. There will be eight stops.

b.

Town A   Town B

2. a. There will be 16 stops.

b.

Town A   Town B

3.

Stop Number	1	2	3	4	5	6	7	8	9	10
Proposal I Distance (in mi)	$\frac{3}{4}$	$1\frac{1}{2}$	$2\frac{1}{4}$	3	$3\frac{3}{4}$	$4\frac{1}{2}$	$5\frac{1}{4}$	6	$6\frac{3}{4}$	$7\frac{1}{2}$
Proposal II Distance (in mi)	$\frac{3}{8}$	$\frac{3}{4}$	$1\frac{1}{8}$	$1\frac{1}{2}$	$1\frac{7}{8}$	$2\frac{1}{4}$	$2\frac{5}{8}$	3	$3\frac{3}{8}$	$3\frac{3}{4}$

For the second row, $\frac{3}{8}$, students should use the map they marked for problem 2. You might want to recommend that students draw number lines to help them fill in the rest of the table.

Extension

Have students make ratio tables as in problem 3 for other fractions. They may use number lines to help them find the answers. Here are some examples with fractions, $\frac{1}{3}$, $\frac{5}{12}$, $\frac{3}{10}$, and $\frac{5}{8}$.

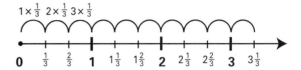

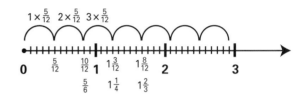

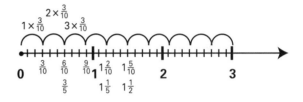

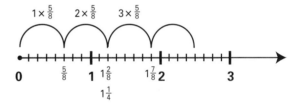

Fraction Division

During a marathon run, you have to drink enough water to stay hydrated. Volunteers along the race course hand out plastic cups of water. One cup holds about $\frac{1}{8}$ liter.

1. Susan's trainer suggests that she drink a total of $2\frac{1}{2}$ liters during the race. How many cups should she grab throughout the race? Show your work.

For allergies, Noelle's doctor prescribed $\frac{1}{4}$ of a tablet, three times a day. Today, there are 12 tablets left until she needs a refill.

2. How many days will these 12 tablets last her? Show your work.

Here is the way Mark calculates $1\frac{3}{4} \div \frac{1}{8}$.

3. Explain Mark's strategy.

$1\frac{3}{4} \div \frac{1}{8} =$

$\frac{7}{4} \div \frac{1}{8} =$

$\frac{14}{8} \div \frac{1}{8} = 14$

Mark

4. Use Mark's strategy to calculate:
   a. $3\frac{1}{3} \div \frac{1}{6}$ b. $2\frac{1}{7} \div \frac{1}{14}$

Mark uses the same strategy to divide by a mixed number. For example, $4\frac{3}{4} \div 1\frac{1}{8}$.

$4\frac{3}{4} \div 1\frac{1}{8} =$

$\frac{19}{4} \div \frac{9}{8} =$

$\frac{38}{8} \div \frac{9}{8} =$

$38 \div 9 = 4\frac{2}{9}$

Mark

5. Use Mark's strategy to calculate:
   a. $5\frac{1}{6} \div 1\frac{1}{3}$ b. $3\frac{1}{10} \div 2\frac{1}{5}$

1. Susan should pick up 20 cups. Sample student work:

One liter holds 8 cups ($8 \times \frac{1}{8} = 1$). So 2 liters contain 16 cups, and $\frac{1}{2}$ of a liter contains 4 cups.

2. Noel's medicine will last 16 more days. Sample student work: One tablet is four doses, ($4 \times \frac{1}{4}$ of a tablet = 1 tablet). Twelve tablets provide for 48 doses (12×4). Since Noel takes the medicine three times a day, 48 doses will last 16 days ($48 \div 3$).

3. Mark thought of one as $\frac{4}{4}$, so $1 + \frac{3}{4} = \frac{4}{4} + \frac{3}{4} = \frac{7}{4}$.

In the third line, he realized that $\frac{7}{4} = \frac{14}{8}$.

If you divide 14 parts of $\frac{1}{8}$ each by one part of $\frac{1}{8}$ each, the result is 14.

4. a.

$$3\frac{1}{3} \div \frac{1}{6} =$$

$$\frac{10}{3} \div \frac{1}{6} =$$

$$\frac{20}{6} \div \frac{1}{6} =$$

$$20 \div 1 = 20$$

b.

$$2\frac{1}{7} \div \frac{1}{14} =$$

$$\frac{15}{7} \div \frac{1}{14} =$$

$$\frac{30}{14} \div \frac{1}{14} =$$

$$30 \div 1 = 30$$

5. a.

$$5\frac{1}{6} \div 1\frac{1}{3} =$$

$$\frac{31}{6} \div \frac{4}{3} =$$

$$\frac{31}{6} \div \frac{8}{6} =$$

$$31 \div 8 = 3\frac{7}{8}$$

$$3\frac{1}{10} \div 2\frac{1}{5} =$$

$$\frac{31}{10} \div \frac{11}{5} =$$

$$\frac{31}{10} \div \frac{22}{10} =$$

$$31 \div 22 = 1\frac{9}{22}$$

With and Without a Calculator

1. Use your calculator to find the cost of the following items. Note that stores round up all prices to the nearest cent.

   a. 1.365 kilograms of pears at $3.10 per kilogram

   b. 0.723 kg of broccoli at $3.25 per kilogram

   c. 1.739 kg of collard greens at $1.79 per kilogram

   d. 1.396 kg of strawberries at $1.65 per kilogram

   e. 0.842 kg of oranges at $2.98 per kilogram

Michelle is supposed to use her calculator to do her homework, but the decimal point key is broken. To calculate the price of 1.293 kg of spinach that costs $2.98 per kilogram, Michelle enters 1293 × 298, and her calculator displays 385314. She can then figure out where to place the decimal point by estimating the correct answer.

2. Without using your calculator, find the answer to 1.293 × $2.98. Explain your strategy.

3. Without using your calculator, help Michelle find the correct price for each of the following items.

   a. 3.129 kg of grapes, selling for $3.10 per kilogram (Michelle's calculator displays 969990.)

   b. 21.38 kg of apples, selling for $1.26 per kilogram (Michelle's calculator displays 269388)

   c. 0.729 kg of lemons, selling for $4.10 per kilogram (Michelle's calculator displays 298890.)

   d. 3.28 kg of oranges, selling for $4.98 per kilogram (Michelle's calculator displays 163344.)

   e. 0.083 kg of parsley, selling for $5.50 per kilogram (Michelle's calculator displays 45650).

1. **a.** $4.24

   b. $2.35

   c. $3.12

   d. $2.31

   e. $2.51

Note: You might need to remind students to round UP in all cases.

2. $3.86 Sample explanation:

   The first number has three decimals and the second number has two decimals. Thus I know the answer has five decimals (3.85314). Since this number represents a price in dollars, I had to round up to the nearest cent.

3. **a.** $9.70

   b. $26.94

   c. $2.99

   d. $16.34

   e. $0.46

Estimations

Animations

To make an animation, you need many pictures to show movement. Hand-drawn animations need 12 frames per second.

1. Estimate how many pictures you will need to draw for a 5-minute cartoon.

Leaking Faucet

Each second, two drops drip from this leaking faucet.

It takes 20 drops to fill one cubic centimeter. Recall that 1 liter fits exactly into one cubic decimeter. Pete's father puts a 10-liter bucket under the tap to catch the water.

2. Will this bucket be large enough to catch all the water during the night, from 8 P.M. till 8 A.M.? Justify your opinion.

New York Marathon

About 30,000 runners sign up to run in the annual New York Marathon.

3. Estimate how long the line of 30,000 participating runners might be. Show your assumptions.

4. A reporter at the race stated that more than two million spectators stood along the route. Does this number make sense? Show your reasoning.

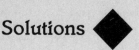
1. Estimated: 10 frames × 60 seconds × 5 minutes ⟶ 3,000 frames.
   12 frames per second is 720 frames per minute (12 × 60).
   For 5 minutes, you need 3,600 frames (5 × 720 or 3,500 + 100).

2. Yes, this is enough for the 12 hours. Sample student reasoning:
   One liter or 1 cubic decimeter is 1,000 cubic centimeters (10 cm × 10 cm × 10 cm).
   A 10-liter bucket will hold 10,000 cubic centimeters. It takes 10 seconds to fill one
   cubic centimeter (2 drops per second for 20 drops). There are 100,000 seconds
   before the bucket is full. Will this cover the 12 hours? One hour is 3600 seconds, so
   ten hours is 36,000 seconds. With only two hours left, we have more than enough
   time before the bucket is full.

   2 drops per second $\xrightarrow{\times\ 60\ \text{sec/min}}$ 120 drops per minute $\xrightarrow{\div\ 20\ \text{drops/cm}^3}$

   60 cm³/min $\xrightarrow{\times\ 60\ \text{min/hr}}$ 360 cm³/hr $\xrightarrow{\times\ 12\ \text{hours}}$ 4,320 cm³/12 hours $\xrightarrow{\div\ 1,000\ \text{cm}^3\text{/liter}}$

   4.32 liters/12 hours

3. About 3 km, but accept any estimation that is based on reasonable assumptions.
   Sample student reasoning:
   The race usually begins on a city street. A street is about 20 meters wide, and
   about 10 people fit across the street. One arrangement of 30,000 people, with 10
   people across, is 3,000 people long. Allowing about 1 meter per person, the length
   of the line is about 3,000 meters or 3 km.

4. Accept any student reasoning based on reasonable assumptions.
   Two sample strategies:
   The number of spectators is not reasonable.
   I assume spectators are on both sides of the course. I also assume that spectators
   standing next to each other occupy one meter per person.

   The marathon is about 40 km, which equals 40,000 m. If all spectators are standing
   in one line on both sides of the track, there could have been about 80,000 people
   (2 × 40,000). If there were more than two million spectators, you would need
   nearly 30 times as many people, 30 × 80,000 is 2,400,000.

   The race is about 40 km or 40,000 m. With spectators on both sides of the race, the
   total length of the spectators is 80,000 m. Since it is very crowded, you can assume
   2 people taking up 1 meter, so I would estimate about 160,000 people along the
   race course. If you allow for 7 rows of spectators along each side, you would have
   14 people every meter on each side of the course. So you would have 2,240,000
   people (14 × 160,000 people).

Extension
How much water will be wasted over a year if the faucet keeps leaking?

Serial Numbers

The Green Air factory makes refrigerators.

A serial number is etched into each refrigerator in sequential order. Here are the serial numbers of the first three refrigerators made last Tuesday.

SR–341–05–0193

SR–341–05–0194

SR–341–05–0195

1. List the last four digits of the serial numbers of the next three refrigerators made at the Green Air factory.

Here are the serial numbers of the last three refrigerators made last Tuesday.

SR–341–05–3601

SR–341–05–3602

SR–341–05–3603

2. How many refrigerators were made last Tuesday?

Last Wednesday, the serial number SR–341–05–3604 was etched into the first refrigerator made, and the last refrigerator made had the serial number SR–341–05–7702.

3. How many refrigerators were made last Wednesday?

The last refrigerator made on Thursday had the serial number SR–341–05–9871, and the last refrigerator made on Friday had the serial number SR–341–06–3004.

4. How many refrigerators were made on Thursday? And on Friday?

Note: In order to do these problems, students should realize that they have to treat the serial numbers like regular numbers. For example, SR–341–05–0193 should be treated like 341,050,193.

1. SR–341–05–0196

   SR–341–05–0197

   SR–341–05–0198

2. 3,411

   A subtraction is 341,053,603 − 341,053,192. This can be simplified to 3,603 − 192. Students might subtract 3,603 − 193, but this is incorrect because the number 0193 is one of the refrigerators produced on this day.

   Others might use the list of problem 1, to realize they can subtract the serial numbers but must add on 1 at the end; 3,603 − 193 + 1.

3. 4,099

   Two possible subtractions: 7,702 − 3,603 or 7,702 − 3,604 + 1

4. Thursday: 2,169

   Friday: 3,133

   For this problem, students have to look at problem 3 in order to find out the serial number of the last refrigerator produced on the previous day.

   Two possible subtraction for Thursday is 9,871 − 7,702 or 9,871 − 7,703 + 1

   For Friday, students should take note that 05 became 06 in the serial number. Because of this change, students have to carry the numbers out to the tens of thousands when subtracting. The correct subtraction is 63,004 − 59,871.

Extension

You might want to challenge students by asking, *What number comes after SR-341–99–9999?* (The next number would be SR-342–00–0000.)

Bar Code (page 1)

Almost all products sold today have a bar code. For retail items, the bar code has a length of 13 digits. It shows information about the county of origin, the manufacturer, and the product. The last digit is a safeguard to check the other twelve digits.

This barcode has only twelve digits; it is missing the safeguard digit.

1122334455bb?

1. Carry out these calculations to find the missing last digit.

   Step 1 Starting from the left, add all digits in the odd position.

   Step 2 Multiply the result by 3.

   Step 3 Add all digits in the even position.

   Step 4 Add the results of Step 2 and Step 3.

   Step 5 Determine what number needs to be added to the result of Step 4 to make it divisible by 10.

Here is a different barcode.

2. Verify that this bar code has a correct safeguard digit.

0 1 2 3 4 5 6 7 8 9 0 0 5

Here is a copy of the barcode for a new book.

ISBN 0-03-040384-7
90000
9 780030 40384?

3. Find the correct safeguard digit for this book.

1. The missing digit is 6.

Step 1	$1 + 2 + 3 + 4 + 5 + 6 = 21$
Step 2	$3 \times 21 = 63$
Step 3	$1 + 2 + 3 + 4 + 5 + 6 = 21$
Step 4	$63 + 21 = 84$
Step 5	add 6 to get to 90.

2.

Step 1	$0 + 2 + 4 + 6 + 8 + 0 = 20$
Step 2	$3 \times 20 = 60$
Step 3	$1 + 3 + 5 + 7 + 9 + 0 = 25$
Step 4	$60 + 25 = 85$
Step 5	Add 5 to get to 90; the safeguard digit is accurate.

3.

Step 1	$9 + 8 + 0 + 0 + 0 + 8 = 25$
Step 2	$3 \times 25 = 75$
Step 3	$7 + 0 + 3 + 4 + 3 + 4 = 21$
Step 4	$75 + 21 = 96$
Step 5	add 4 to get 100, the safeguard digit should be a 4.

Bar Code (page 2)

There is also an ISBN number located across the top of the barcode. This number contains information about the country, the publisher, and the title of the book. The last digit is the safeguard digit.

The safeguard digit for an ISBN code is calculated differently from the safeguard digit of the barcode below it.

4. Use the following steps to find the safeguard digit of the ISBN number 90–270–1165-?

    Step 1: Multiply the first digit by 10,
    the second digit by 9,
    the third digit by 8,
    and so on. Then add the results.

    Step 2: Determine what number you have to add to the result in Step 1 to make it evenly divisible by 11.

5. Verify that this book, *Number Tools*, has a correct safeguard digit for the ISBN number.

    Here is some additional information you might find interesting.

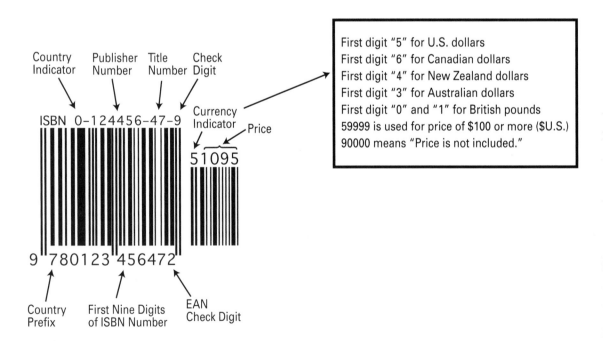

First digit "5" for U.S. dollars
First digit "6" for Canadian dollars
First digit "4" for New Zealand dollars
First digit "3" for Australian dollars
First digit "0" and "1" for British pounds
59999 is used for price of $100 or more ($U.S.)
90000 means "Price is not included."

6. Look for another book and use this information to decode its barcode.

4. The safeguard digit is 5.

Step 1

$(10 \times 9) + (9 \times 0) + (8 \times 2) + (7 \times 7) +$
$(6 \times 0) + (5 \times 1) + (4 \times 1) + (3 \times 6) +$
$(2 \times 5) = 192$

Step 2

Note that $17 \times 11 = 187$ and $18 \times 11 = 198$;

Add 6 to 192 to make the total divisible by 11, the safeguard digit is 6.

5. Note: This is the ISBN on the back of the *Number Tools* Student Book.

Step 1

$(10 \times 0) + (9 \times 0) + (8 \times 3) + (7 \times 0) +$
$(6 \times 4) + (5 \times 0) + (4 \times 3) + (3 \times 8) +$
$(2 \times 4) = 24 + 24 + 12 + 24 + 8 = 92$

Step 2

$9 \times 11 = 99$
add 7 to 92 to get 99.

So the safeguard digit is correct.

6. Have students check each other's answers.